Hi! My name is Buzzbee. I'll be your guide through Roadmaps. Write your name, age, and today's date, so everyone will know that this is YOUR Roadmaps workbook.

My name is

_____

My age is

_____

I started this workbook on

_____

Your Roadmaps workbook is private. But you can share it with other people, like your parents. Take good care of it and keep it in a safe place.

PRIVATE PROPERTY! NO TRESPASSING!

Roadmaps to Recovery

A Guided Workbook for Children in Treatment

SECOND EDITION

Timothy J. Kahn, MSW

Safer Society Press
Brandon, VT

Editorial Director & Development: Gaen Murphree
Copy Editor: Susannah Noel
Project Manager & Proofreader: Collette Leonard
Illustrator: Sue Storey
Designer: Peter Holm, Sterling Hill Productions
Design Assistant: Abrah Griggs, Sterling Hill Productions

Printed in the United States of America, June 2021

Library of Congress Cataloging-in-Publication Data
Kahn, Timothy J.

   Roadmaps to recovery : a guided workbook for children in treatment / Timothy J. Kahn. -- 2nd ed.
     p. cm.
   ISBN 978-1-884444-77-7
  1. Psychosexual disorders in children. I. Title.

RJ506.P72K34 2007
618.92'8583--dc22

              2007032402

PO Box 340
Brandon, Vermont 05733
www.safersocietypress.org
(802) 247-3132

Safer Society Press is a program of the Safer Society Foundation, a 501(c)3 nonprofit dedicated to the prevention and treatment of sexual abuse. For more information, visit our Web site at www.safersociety.org.

Roadmaps to Recovery: A Guided Workbook for Children in Treatment, Second Edition

Order # WP122

Dedication

This second edition of *Roadmaps to Recovery* is dedicated
to all of the children who find the courage and strength to complete their
treatment and become responsible, caring members of society. You are all true
Survivors! It is also dedicated to the many parents, foster parents, and staff
members who spend countless hours helping children overcome past traumas
to learn new skills for happy and successful lives.

A Note of Thanks

This book was written with the help of many young boys and girls who worked very hard to learn to control their sexual behavior problems. You know who you are, and I am very proud of you all.

I would also like to thank the many staff members in Cottage A (WINGS Program) and Cottage D (SOAR Program) at Ryther Child Center in Seattle, Washington, for their dedication to working with boys and girls with sexual behavior problems and their help in developing this second edition of the *Roadmaps* workbook. I would like to particularly thank Jill Latteri, MSW, and Robert Strauss, MSW, for their suggestions, guidance, and experience in using the *Roadmaps* material in their treatment programs. Erica Smith, BA, and Monica Kristiansen, MA, also provided helpful feedback and ideas. In addition, Matt Platte, MEd, provided many helpful suggestions and ideas.

I would also like to thank my associates, Krishan Hansen, MSW, Carol Almero, MA, Brent (B. J.) Oneal, PhD, Larraine Lynch, MSW, Valarie Mitchell, MSW, and Jo Langford-Fuchs, MA, for their ongoing helpful suggestions and feedback.

Many of the changes in this second edition of *Roadmaps* are based on the input and ideas of all the persons listed above. I would also like to express my heartfelt thanks and appreciation to my editor, Gaen Murphree, for the countless hours of dialogue that have gone on "behind the scenes" in order to produce this workbook. Her ideas and thoughts are incorporated on every page, and her enthusiasm for this project has been inspiring and motivating.

My wife, DeeAnn, continues to provide much support and encouragement for all of my work, including this project. Thank you!

Contents

A Note to Counselors

When *Roadmaps to Recovery: A Guided Workbook for Young People in Treatment* was first published in 1999, professionals treating children with sexual behavior problems were facing a field with little research base and limited clinical experience. Over the past eight years of using *Roadmaps to Recovery*, we have found that parts of the workbook were very helpful to children with sexual behavior problems and their parents, whereas other parts were less helpful. With input from many other professionals, I have completely reworked the *Roadmaps to Recovery* workbook for this new edition, striving to keep the most helpful elements, eliminate the less helpful elements, and incorporate important components of promising evidenced-based interventions, specifically trauma-focused cognitive behavioral therapy (TF-CBT). It is my hope that this completely revised second edition provides a trauma-sensitive intervention that supports development of resiliency and provides a strength-based modality for helping children change hurtful or problematic behavior patterns, while learning adaptive and healthy skills for productive and caring interpersonal relationships.

Those of you who've been working with the first edition of *Roadmaps to Recovery* will find many changes. Entirely new to the second edition are simple, rewarding tests at the end of each chapter that provide a way to increase a child's retention of materials, as well as an additional opportunity to reward their hard work. Additionally, there is an all-new chapter on being a survivor and increased attention to learning to overcome past traumas. You will also find that many of the chapters have been reordered (for example, the chapter on managing sexual feelings is now the sixth rather than the thirteenth) in response to what we have found to be most effective in treatment. This new edition includes expanded information about puberty, a topic that most children find very interesting. Chapters that had proven to be less helpful in treatment (such as the first edition's "Building Up My Walls to Stop Wrong Touching" and "Understanding My Cycles") have been entirely reconceptualized and rewritten. The concluding chapter on creating a Safety Plan Book contains largely all-new material. Buzzbee's role as a friendly guide and support is also expanded in this edition.

Children with sexual behavior problems are a diverse group, and the age range of six to twelve can represent many different levels of ability and attention. We have found from our past work with *Roadmaps to Recovery* that it is helpful to have the client read the first few paragraphs of the workbook out loud to you, so that you can get a good idea of how well they read. If they have difficulty with the reading, it is usually very supportive and helpful for the counselor to offer to do the reading out loud to the client.

Writing is also sometimes difficult for this population, and offering to write the answers to assignments in the workbook for the client is often perceived by clients as a very friendly, supportive, and caring gesture. When counselors do the writing, it is a good idea to have the client initial the page at the bottom so that they feel they have an important job to do in keeping track of their progress through the workbook. Children get a sense of pride and accomplishment when they help sign the pages. The second edition provides two check boxes for your initials and your client's initials at the bottom of every page. These check boxes not only help involve children in the process of reading and completing the workbook, but they also help both client and counselor keep track of where you are in *Roadmaps to Recovery*. Additionally, I recommend sitting at a desk or table with the client, so that the client can read along with you and participate in completing the exercises.

Much thought has been given to helping clients stay motivated. Several of the chapters have built-in breaks because they contain difficult or lengthy material. Since this population is so diverse, counselors should feel free to build in other breaks anytime they feel a client is losing interest or getting tired. At the end of each chapter, children are told to ask their counselor for a high-five or a sticker. This gives counselors a choice of different reinforcements to use, and counselors may wish to keep a supply of stickers on hand in order to reward clients after their hard work. Of course, some counselors may want to use their own reinforcement as well, which is encouraged. At the end of each chapter, children are also told to fill in their progress chart. You'll find the progress chart at the back of the workbook. The chart has been designed to give clients even more recognition for their hard work. Given how emotionally difficult some of the work in *Roadmaps to Recovery* can be, counselors are encouraged to use strong, frequent reinforcers.

This workbook contains some graphic references to sexual behaviors that some children engage in. While I have attempted to limit such specific details so that we don't introduce ideas that children don't already have, there is no getting around the fact that children working in *Roadmaps* will learn about the correct terms for body parts and some sexual activities. If a parent or child objects to a particular term, counselors are encouraged to substitute another appropriate term when reading the workbook to the child. For example, one young boy was taught by his parents to never use the word *penis*. In his case, he was more comfortable using the word *private*, and it reduced some of the child's anxiety for the counselor to make that substitution when reading the book to him. Counselors are encouraged to consider the individual needs of each client and family and make such changes if needed.

Counselors are also encouraged to involve parents in the counseling process. It is very important that parents also learn the same skills and knowledge that their children are being taught. It is usually most helpful when parents have an opportunity to review the workbook before children start working in it. This gives each parent a chance to learn about what will be taught to their children and to discuss any questions or concerns before their child starts the workbook. Many of the concepts taught in *Roadmaps* work best when parents or caregivers support practice and repetition of the skills at home.

The Safer Society Foundation also publishes a parents' guide for the *Roadmaps* and *Pathways* workbooks, and that guide can be very helpful at encouraging parents to become involved in the counseling process. The parents' guide for *Roadmaps* contains a great deal of general treatment information, as well as specific questions parents can ask their children as each chapter is completed.

Roadmaps is designed for the child's work to culminate in the creation of the Safety Plan Book, which incorporates what the client has learned into a personal notebook of reminders, skill steps, and other helpful information. The Safety Plan Book supports the clients both by helping them review what they have learned and by giving them something concrete and portable that they can then show to new caregivers, teachers, counselors, or other support persons. Chapter 16 contains instructions for creating this Safety Plan Book. As a counselor, you may choose to start the Safety Plan Book early in your *Roadmaps* work, or you can wait until you reach chapter 16 and use it as the final project. I recommend that counselors review chapter 16 before they begin any work with a new client.

I have found it helpful to start working on and building the Safety Plan book very early in the *Roadmaps* process, even as early as chapter 1. Any time a counselor is covering what may be considered key skill areas with a client, consider making a list or drawing of those skill steps and putting them into a three-ring notebook so the client is continually working to build their own Safety Plan Book. I have found that printing out reminders of skill steps in a large font can be very helpful to children. Children then take those pages, decorate them, and organize them in their three-ring binders with plastic sheet protectors. Children should be encouraged to personalize their Safety Plan Book, and they should be encouraged to be creative with it. It is also important that they be encouraged to bring the Safety Plan Book to each counseling session so that it can be updated and revised on a regular basis. On a practical note, it is helpful to provide the three-ring notebook and plastic sheet holders. It is also helpful to have colored paper, markers, and other art supplies on hand to help make the Safety Plan Book more attractive.

I encourage counselors to e-mail feedback or ideas to me (timothykahn@cs.com) in order to further refine and improve the *Roadmaps* workbook. I would very much like to hear about what is working and what could be improved for future revisions of *Roadmaps*.

I personally wish you the best in working with this population of young people. I have found much inspiration and reward in helping children overcome their histories of trauma and inappropriate learning experiences. I am continually impressed with how hard children will work to learn new skills and develop new knowledge. I have now been working in this field long enough to see clients I knew as children grow up, get married, have their own children, and live productive and successful lives. With support and guidance from professionals such as yourself, we have every reason to believe that the future of the children we work with is very bright.

Timothy Kahn, MSW
Bellevue, Washington

CHAPTER 1

Start Your Engines

Hello! Welcome to *Roadmaps to Recovery*, a workbook for boys and girls ages 6 to 12 with touching problems.

You are reading this workbook because somebody wants to help you learn to control your body, your thinking, and your feelings so that you will not get into trouble as you get older.

Learning to change your behavior can be hard work. This workbook will be your four-wheel-drive Jeep to help you get over even the worst road. By using this workbook, you will be on the right road to a healthy life!

When you do all your work in *Roadmaps*, you will feel better about yourself. You will be a better problem solver. You will make better choices. You will be proud of your new behavior and new skills. And people who care about you will be proud of all the good things you have learned and done.

Remember: You are not alone. Other boys and girls have touching problems too. They have also gotten help for their touching problems. They have learned how to control their touching problems, and you can too. And just like them, you can learn new skills and prepare yourself for a happy and successful life.

This workbook is yours to keep, so you will want to take good care of it. You might decide to take this workbook home so that you can work on it there. If you do take it home, you will need to remember to bring it back to your counselor's office. You might also decide to leave it in your counselor's office. Talk to your counselor about where you want to keep it.

At the bottom of each page you will see two small boxes. After you finish reading and doing the work on each page, put your initials in one of the boxes. Your counselor will then put his or her initials in the other box. This will help you keep track of where you are in *Roadmaps.*

With help from your counselor, parent, foster parent, or group home staff, try to do a little bit of *Roadmaps* every day or at least every week. It might take a long time to finish *Roadmaps,* but that is OK! It takes time to learn and practice new behaviors. Did you jump on a bike and ride it the first time you tried? Probably not—it takes lots of practice to learn new things.

To keep track of how well you're doing on your travels through *Roadmaps,* you'll find a progress chart at the back of this book. At the

end of each chapter, you'll get to fill in your progress chart and get a sticker or a high-five from your counselor. The chart helps you see where you are on your *Roadmaps* journey. The sticker or high-five is a way of saying, "Congratulations for sharing with your counselor and working hard! Look at the great job you're doing!"

Your counselor, parent, foster parent, or group home staff may want to set up other rewards for you as you finish assignments and chapters.

When you have completed this workbook, you will get to join

the Sexual Abuse Prevention and Safety Team! Lots of other young people around the world who are living healthy lives have joined the team. Each page, each assignment, and each chapter you complete will bring you closer to being on the team. And each step you take as you work through

Roadmaps will also bring you closer to being a Survivor. This means that you will have survived your past bad experiences and learned how to live a happy and healthy life!

Have a great trip through *Roadmaps* with Buzzbee as your guide! Good luck with your travels in *Roadmaps!*

Now, here is your first assignment! This is so your counselor can get to know you a little bit, and you will get to know yourself even better. *Roadmaps* can help in all parts of your life, so it is important to learn about who you are and how you think.

As you do your assignments in *Roadmaps,* you can write your answers right in this book. You probably learned the rule about not writing in books. But this is your *Roadmaps* workbook, and it is OK to write and draw in it. If you need help writing down your answers, you can ask your counselor for help. Lots of kids using *Roadmaps* are still learning to write, so asking for help is OK!

Assignment 1A

Please answer the following questions about yourself.

What is your full name?_____

What is your birth date?_____

What grade are you in?_____

What school do you go to?_____

Where do you live right now?_____

Who do you live with?_____

What do you like to eat the most?_____

Assignment 1A (continued)

What do you like to do in your free time?_____

_____

What do you want to do when you grow up?_____

_____

Do you have any brothers or sisters?

❑ Yes   ❑ No

If you checked yes, write down the names and ages of your brothers
and sisters:

Name   Age

_____   _____

_____   _____

_____   _____

_____   _____

Do you have any pets right now?

❑ Yes   ❑ No

If yes, what type of pets do you have (dog, cat, snake, gerbil, goldfish,
or another animal) and what are their names?

Type   Name of Pet

_____   _____

_____   _____

_____   _____

Assignment 1A (continued)

Have you ever used a computer by yourself?

❏ Yes   ❏ No

If yes, have you ever been on the Internet by yourself?

❏ Yes   ❏ No

What do you like to do on the Internet?_____

_____

Who is your best friend right now?_____

_____

Who do you tell your secrets to?_____

Who in the whole world do you respect (look up to) the most right now?_____

Who do you want to be just like when you grow up?

_____

You are doing great! You are on the right road for safety!

Assignment 1B

In the space below, draw a picture of you, your pets, your house, and your family. Then add other drawings or words about your favorite foods, things you like to do in your free time, and so on. In the drawing, try to put in as much stuff from Assignment 1A as you can. You may use pictures or words. Have fun!

Great job! You have just taken the first step toward joining the Sexual Abuse Prevention and Safety Team!

Now you are ready for your first Road Test. Grab a pencil and give it your best. Road Test 1 is open book. That means it's OK to look things up as you go. Good luck!

I'm proud of you for getting off to such a good start!

ROAD TEST 1

Start Your Engines
(open book)

Name:_____

Date:_____

9 points possible. 8 points needed for passing.

Total Score:___/9   ❑ Pass   ❑ Need more work

1. By completing this workbook, you will be able to join the Sexual Abuse Prevention and Safety Team. (1 point)

       ❑ True   ❑ False

2. Many boys and girls are now getting help for their sexual touching problems. (1 point)

       ❑ True   ❑ False

3. Learning to change your behavior can be hard work. (1 point)

❑ True   ❑ False

4. You can learn to control your touching with another person. (1 point)

❑ True   ❑ False

5. What have you learned from reading this first chapter in *Roadmaps*? (2 points)

_____

_____

_____

6. Who in the whole world do you respect (look up to) the most right now? Explain why you respect this person. (2 points)

_____

_____

_____

7. What is your counselor's name? (1 point)

_____

You're off to a great start in *Roadmaps!* Fill in your progress chart for chapter 1 and get a sticker or a high-five from your counselor.

CHAPTER 2

What Is a Touching Problem?

Warning: Read This Now! Some kids have very strong feelings when they work on their touching problems in *Roadmaps.* Some kids get mad or sad. Some kids want to hit something. Some kids get very strong sexual feelings in their minds and in their private parts.

These feelings are all normal, but hitting something or doing some sexual behavior can get you into trouble. Here are some ideas to help you stay out of trouble.

1. Tell your counselor about your feelings before you do anything with them.

2. Do something to move your body. Do sit-ups, play basketball, run around the block or your yard or a parking lot, or jump rope. Doing something physical helps make sad, mad, or sexual feelings go away.

3. Stop your work in *Roadmaps* for a little while and tell an adult you trust about your feelings. An adult will help you get back on the right road and back into *Roadmaps* when you are ready.

This could be a bumpy road, so fasten your seat belts and get a good person to help steer you through!

Assignment 2A

Make a list of all the adults in your life you can tell when you are feeling mad or sad or having sexual feelings.

1. _____

2. _____

3. _____

4. _____

5. _____

6. _____

As you work through *Roadmaps,* it's good to remember that anybody can have a touching problem, even teenagers and adults. What's more, touching problems are easier to fix when you're younger. So it's great that you are doing *Roadmaps* now. Even though there'll be some bumps in the road, *Roadmaps* will help steer you through to a healthy and happy life.

Here's what it was like for Levi, a 10-year-old boy who finished the *Roadmaps* workbook:

> *Roadmaps* made me think about things I didn't want to think about, and it helped me to talk about things that were hard to talk about. Sometimes when I had those bad thoughts, I also had bad behavior. *Roadmaps* taught me how to handle disappointments, and it taught me how to stay out of trouble. If I can do it, you

can do it too. With a little hard work, you can learn how to overcome your problems and live a safe life. Remember, don't give up. When I first learned to ride a bike, I sometimes fell down. I always got up and tried again, and now I can ride really well. *Roadmaps* was kind of like that for me. I sometimes made mistakes, but I kept trying to do my best, and I finally found out how to have a healthy life. I have learned how to be a Survivor.

A *touching problem* is when one person touches another person without permission. Some touching problems are called sexual behavior problems. A *sexual behavior problem* is when somebody touches somebody else's private parts without permission or when the person being touched is too young to know what's going on.

Sexual behavior problems can also include touching your own private parts in public places, talking too much about private parts, looking at too many pictures of naked people, or spying on other people when they are undressing. Another type of sexual behavior problem is when a person pulls down the pants or takes off the clothes of another person without permission. Rubbing up against a person's private parts or pretending to have sex with another person can also be a sexual behavior problem.

Private parts are a person's bottom, chest, penis, vulva, and vagina. If you are not sure what those words mean, ask your counselor. We will explain them more in other chapters. Your private parts are also called *sexual parts*. Sexual parts are parts of the body that have to do with sex. Sex is not bad, but some sexual touching is called Wrong Touching because it can hurt the other person or get you into trouble.

In *Roadmaps* you will get lots of help to stop any Wrong Touching or sexual behavior problems that you may have. You will also learn skills for making healthy and good relationships with other people.

There are other kinds of touching problems and sexual behavior problems besides the ones already mentioned.

Some boys and girls touch their pet animals in their private parts or hurt animals by being too rough with them. This can sometimes be a sexual behavior problem, or just a touching problem. Some boys and girls look at pictures of naked people in magazines or on the Internet, and some boys and girls draw pictures of private parts. Some boys and girls spend too much time talking about sex. Some boys and girls touch their own private parts so much that they start to hurt. All of these things can sometimes cause problems, so they might be called sexual behavior problems.

It is a sexual behavior problem when someone touches the private parts of another person who doesn't want to be touched, or when the other person is too young. It is also a sexual behavior problem when someone uses tricks or bribes to do sexual touching. It is always a sexual behavior problem when a person hurts another person by touching their private parts.

Another type of touching problem is called *incest*. Incest is when people in the same family (except parents) touch each other's private parts. Incest is illegal, or against the law. One reason is that if babies were made, they might have physical or mental problems. Another reason is that it hurts younger people when older people do sexual touching with them before they're old enough to understand. That is why people should **not** do sexual touching with other people in the same family.

Not all sexual touching is wrong. In fact, one kind of sexual touching is how babies are made. Sexual touching can be fun and exciting when you're old enough. This kind of good sexual touching only happens when both people are old enough and both give their permission.

So sexual touching can be a very good thing. It is not a good thing, however, when young children do it, or when it hurts or bothers other people.

Some kinds of Wrong Sexual Touching are illegal, or against the law, and people who do Wrong Sexual Touching can get arrested by the police and can even go to jail. Children don't go to adult jails, but children who do Wrong Sexual Touching can go to special jails for children where they have to stay while they get help for their touching problems. These

places are called *kids' jail, juvenile detention,* or *juvie.*

Roadmaps will help you learn to control all of your touching problems so that you will not get in trouble when you grow up.

There is one other problem that is kind of like a touching problem. It is a type of sexual behavior problem called *sexual harassment*. Sexual harassment is when a person says or does something sexual or personal that bothers another person. Here are some examples of sexual harassment:

Calling someone a sexual name.

Asking someone to do sexual touching when they have said "no" before.

Telling a sexual joke that bothers other people.

Showing sexual pictures to someone who doesn't want to see them.

Talking about a person's sexual body parts.

Talking about a person's sexual behavior.

For example, one boy got into trouble at school for talking about the size of a girl's breasts on the school bus. The bus driver heard the boy and reported him to the principal. The boy embarrassed the girl and made her feel bad. His behavior was sexual harassment, and he was suspended from school so that all the girls at school and on the bus would feel more safe.

Sexual harassment is not a good thing. People do sexual harassment to make someone else feel bad, or to get someone to do something they don't want to do. Boys and girls can get into big trouble for it. You might get kicked out of school. When you get older, you might get fired from a job for doing sexual harassment at work.

Assignment 2B

Write down your own example of sexual harassment:

_____

_____

_____

_____

_____

In *Roadmaps* you sometimes work one-on-one with a counselor, and you sometimes work together with a counselor and a group of other kids who also have touching and sexual behavior problems.

Counselors know how to help kids and grownups in lots of different ways. Your counselor can teach you how to control your body, your feelings, and your thinking so you will **not** do Wrong Touching when you grow up.

Groups are when 3 or more people sit down together with a counselor to talk about their problems. Groups help boys and girls with touching problems feel like they are not alone. Groups help boys and girls learn to control their bodies in good ways. Groups help boys and girls stay out of jail.

Here's what Starlet and Ted had to say about working with their counselors and with their groups:

Hello, my name is Starlet. I am 9 years old. I did some wrong private part touching with my younger brother. I am working hard to learn about Right Touching so that I can stay out of trouble! I have learned to talk about things that happened to me and things that I did to others. I have learned that honesty is the most important thing in *Roadmaps!* I have learned to be honest with my counselor.

Hi, my name is Ted. I had a touching problem. My parents took me to a counselor because I was touching other kids in their private parts. I was about 7 years old when I was doing the private touching. Now I am 10 years old and I haven't done any wrong private part touching for 3 years. You should not be afraid in group. We try and help each other in group. I just told the truth to the other kids and my counselor.

It is sometimes scary to be in a group to talk about private problems. Most boys and girls learn to like groups, because in groups they get support and help. Plus, it feels good to know that you are not alone.

Groups work best when everyone agrees to follow directions and rules. If you are in a group, your counselor may have all the boys and

girls in the group make a list of
rules. Rules make groups a good,
safe place to be.

Here are some rules that you
can learn to help your group be
a safe place and to show that you
care about and respect the other
group members:

1. Arrive on time, be ready
    on time, and leave on time.

2. Sit still in your chair. Sitting in groups is hard, but it's
    important.

3. Look at the person who is talking.

4. Let one person talk at a time and don't interrupt, make
    wisecracks, or start side conversations with someone else in
    group.

5. Ask questions about what the other group members said. This
    shows you are interested in others.

6. When you hear a group member use Right Thinking, tell them
    they're doing a good thing. When you hear Wrong Thinking,
    try to nicely suggest something that would be Right Thinking.
    We will learn about Wrong Thinking and Right Thinking in
    chapter 5.

When you follow these rules, your group will be a great place, and it
will help you stay out of trouble!

Now it is time to get to know you a little bit more! *Roadmaps* lets you share about yourself by drawing pictures. Have fun!

Assignment 2C

Draw a picture of yourself, as you are right now, in the box below. Don't worry about how good your drawing is.

Assignment 2D

Draw a picture of someone you care about. You can draw more than 1 person. Ask your counselor to help you label each person in the picture. If you want, you can draw on a different piece of paper and cut out the picture and paste it or staple it on this page. Don't worry if you feel you are not very good at drawing—just do your best. This drawing is only for you!

Nice work! Your picture can help you remember that you can care about people and that they can care about you.

Now, let's begin thinking about your biggest problems and your biggest goals. A *problem* is something that makes your life harder, that gets you into trouble with other kids or grownups, or that makes you feel bad. A *goal* is something to work for that makes you feel good and strong inside yourself. Here is a list of problems and goals from a girl named Sherri:

My problem list:

1. I was abused by my uncle.
2. I can't live with my parents.
3. I don't like how I look.
4. I have a touching problem because I touched my brother's private parts.
5. I am not very good in school.

My goal list:

1. I want to get over my past.
2. I want a good place to live.
3. I want to have nicer clothes.
4. I want to get over my touching problems.
5. I want to graduate from high school.

Now it is your turn to make up a list of problems and goals. You might share this list with your group if you have one, or you might just share it with your counselor, parents, foster parents, or group home staff.

Assignment 2E

Make a list of your problems and your goals.

My problem list:

1. _____

2. _____

3. _____

4. _____

5. _____

6. _____

My goal list:

1. _____

2. _____

3. _____

4. _____

5. _____

6. _____

You're doing great, traveling right along to the end of chapter 2! You're following *Roadmaps* to a better life and good adventures!

Time for Road Test 2. Remember, it's open book, so you can use your copy of *Roadmaps* as much as you want.

ROAD TEST 2

What Is a Touching Problem?
(open book)

Name:_____

Date:_____

16 points possible. 15 points needed for passing.

Total Score:___/16   ❑ Pass   ❑ Need more work

1. Buzzbee is a: (1 point)

     A. ___frog.

     B. ___bumblebee.

     C. ___Jeep.

     D. ___bug.

2. All sexual touching is bad, even for adults. (1 point)

     ❑ True   ❑ False

3. Sexual touching is not a good thing when: (1 point)

     A. ____it hurts other people.

     B. ____the other person doesn't want it.

     C. ____someone uses tricks or bribes to do it.

     D. ____All of the above

4. Check all of the things on this list that you think are sexual behavior problems or touching problems. (5 points)

❑ Touching your own private parts in public

❑ Shaking hands with your counselor

❑ Spying on other people who are undressing

❑ Talking about private parts a lot in public

❑ Touching the private parts of a younger brother or sister

❑ Grabbing someone's bottom

❑ Giving your foster mother a hug

5. You can learn to control your touching problems. (1 point)
❑ True   ❑ False

6. Check all the behaviors on this list that are sexual harassment. (5 points)

❑ Calling someone a sexual name

❑ Saying hello to a person

❑ Asking someone to do sexual touching when they have said no before

❑ Telling a sexual joke that bothers other people

❑ Showing someone sexual pictures

❑ Talking about a person's sexual body parts

7. What have you learned from reading this second chapter in *Roadmaps*? (2 points)

_____

_____

_____

_____

_____

_____

_____

Great work on chapter 2! You shared a lot and learned a lot!
Fill in your progress chart and get a sticker or high-five from your counselor.

CHAPTER 3

Learning to Talk About Your Feelings

In this chapter, you will learn how to talk about what is going on in your body and in your thoughts in a healthy way. You will learn about feelings. Everybody has feelings every day. Some people are better at talking about feelings. Some boys and girls only know how to talk about happy or angry feelings. Other boys and girls know how to talk about lots of different feelings. In *Roadmaps* it is very important that you learn to talk about lots of different feelings.

One way to start is to learn about what makes you happy and angry.

Assignment 3A

List 4 things that make you happy.

1. _____

2. _____

3. _____

4. _____

Assignment 3B

Now list 4 things that make you angry.

1. _____

2. _____

3. _____

4. _____

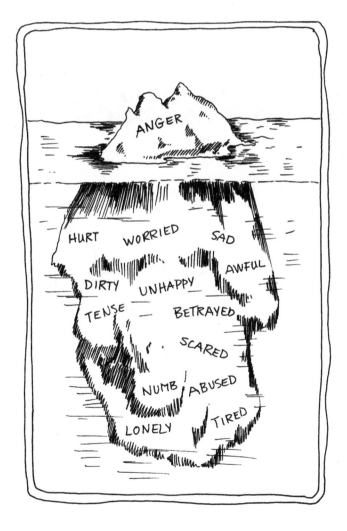

Some children feel mad and angry very often. Sometimes anger can be an excuse for not feeling other feelings. In *Roadmaps* we want you to understand that anger is kind of like an iceberg. Icebergs that you see above the surface of the water are really much larger than they seem to be. Most of the iceberg is under the water. With anger, it is kind of like that: most of the feelings that cause the anger are below the water, or under the surface.

Anger is a normal feeling that most people get sometimes. People who get angry *all* the time can be described as mean or mad. They can also be called aggressive. It is not good to be angry all the time. In fact, it's no fun at all. People who are very angry usually are not very good at talking about their other feelings.

Do you have an anger iceberg? What other feelings might be hidden under the surface?

In *Roadmaps* it is very important to learn to talk about other feelings, not just your happy or angry feelings. Learning to talk about your other feelings is an important part of a healthy and happy life. This next assignment will help you start to talk about other feelings you might have sometimes.

Assignment 3C

List 4 other feelings you sometimes have (such as sad, lonely, scared, sexy, frustrated, curious, loving, hungry, tired, cold, and so on).

1. _____

2. _____

3. _____

4. _____

Will had an anger iceberg. He's 10 and lives in a group home. Will used to get mad a lot, and staff often had to hold him down to keep him from hurting people or breaking things. As Will went through

counseling, he learned that he has lots of other feelings. He is unhappy that his parents abused him, and he feels strange and sad that he doesn't have a regular home to live in. He also feels bad about himself for sexually touching his sister. Will is also very lonely, and he doesn't feel like other kids want him for their friend.

A funny thing has happened. As Will has learned to talk about his life, he has learned about lots of different feelings. Before he started talking about his

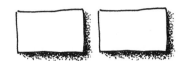

feelings, all he knew was anger. So Will has learned that underneath his anger he had lots of other feelings. Now Will can talk about his feelings and speak up without hurting other people. Will feels a lot better, and he is starting to make friends.

Assignment 3D

In the space below, write down as many feeling words as you can. It is OK to ask for help from your counselor or parents.

_____	_____
_____	_____
_____	_____
_____	_____
_____	_____
_____	_____
_____	_____
_____	_____

Assignment 3E

Now let's play a matching game. Draw a line from each feeling word to the situation that matches the word.

Lonely	Playing with someone I like
Happy	Bedtime
Frustrated	Getting up too early in the morning
Hungry	Not having many friends
Tired	Doing fun things
Grouchy	Getting a hug before I go to bed
Sad	Going to the water park
Unloved	Having a family
Ecstatic	Getting into trouble
Friendly	Seeing the bad guys win on TV
Loving	Lunchtime

Assignment 3F

Think about the last 2 weeks. Using your own experiences, finish these sentences:

1. I felt joyful when _____

2. I felt frustrated when _____

3. I felt loved when _____

4. I felt happy when _____

5. I felt sad when _____

6. I felt confused when _____

7. I felt lonely when _____

8. I felt proud when _____

9. I felt afraid when _____

10. I felt unhappy when _____

You are doing great! Keep it up and you will soon be really good at talking about your feelings!

One of the best things about learning to talk about feelings is that you can learn to ask for what you want without hurting yourself or other people. You can learn to be *assertive,* without being either *passive* or *aggressive.*

Passive means letting things be done to you or not doing anything. Passive people act like nothing is bothering them, and they don't express their feelings. Passive people may have feelings, but they don't like conflict, and they don't like to yell, argue, or fight. Sometimes they let other people make decisions for them, even when it's not what they want. Sometimes people who are passive are really feeling angry, but they don't know it or don't show it.

Aggressive people are pushy and sometimes demanding. They don't think about how their behavior affects other people. Aggressive people sometimes scare other people, because they are loud and sometimes mean. Bullies are often aggressive.

Assertive people say what they think and ask for what they want. They are not passive, they do speak up for themselves, and they

Passive   Aggressive   Assertive

hardly ever let other people make decisions for them. Assertive people express their feelings without hurting or scaring other people.

Assignment 3G

Read the sentence, and then decide if the behavior is passive, aggressive, or assertive. Check the correct answer.

1. Suzy is mad at her foster mom. She wants to call her friend on the phone, but her mom won't let her. She tells her mom that she is upset, and she tells her mom that she wants to talk about it.

     ❏ Passive   ❏ Aggressive   ❏ Assertive

2. Josh is unhappy about his birthday party plans. He decides to sit in his room and listen to his music.

     ❏ Passive   ❏ Aggressive   ❏ Assertive

3. Cory wants to play Nintendo, but his parents have put the controllers away. He yells, "You are never fair!" He then slams the door and kicks a chair, breaking it.

     ❏ Passive   ❏ Aggressive   ❏ Assertive

Assignment 3H

Betty is mad because the staff members at her group home want her to help with the dinner dishes. Write an assertive response for Betty to use.

Assertive Response: _____

_____

_____

_____

Assignment 3I

During the next week, try to be assertive at least 3 different times. Keep track of when you act assertively by telling how you feel and asking for what you want.

1. _____

_____

2. _____

_____

3. _____

_____

In *Roadmaps* we hope you will learn to be more assertive. Passive people don't express their feelings enough, while aggressive people express their feelings in a mean or hurtful way. Assertive people express their feelings clearly, without hurting or scaring other people. Being assertive will help you say how you feel and what you want. This is a big step in learning to live a healthy life. Try to practice this every day. Use your feeling words to say how you feel, and then ask for what you want. This doesn't always work, and you don't always get what you want, but it works a lot better than throwing tantrums or breaking things! Practice makes perfect, so start practicing your assertive skills now. And keep talking about all your different feelings!

ROAD TEST 3

Learning to Talk About Your Feelings
(open book)

Name:_____

Date:_____

8 points possible. 7 points needed for passing.

Total Score:___/8   ❑ Pass   ❑ Need more work

1. Everybody has feelings every day. (1 point)
    ❑ True   ❑ False

2. There are more feelings than just happy or angry. (1 point)
    ❑ True   ❑ False

3. By learning to talk about feelings, you learn to get what you want without
   hurting other people. (1 point)
    ❑ True   ❑ False

4. Passive means loud, active, and yelling. (1 point)
    ❑ True   ❑ False

5. Assertive people say what they think and ask for what they want. (1 point)
    ❑ True   ❑ False

6. Check all the statements on this list that are considered assertive.
(3 points)

❏ John tells his mother that he is tired and he would like to do his laundry tomorrow.

❏ Margie yells at her brother and tells him he is stupid.

❏ Kim refuses to do the dishes and throws the dishtowel on the floor.

❏ Cedric tells his teacher that he has been sick and asks for more time to do his assignment.

❏ Susan tells her friends that she doesn't like John, and she says that she doesn't want to go to the movies with him.

Nice job! Fill in your progress chart and get a sticker or a high-five for this chapter.

CHAPTER 4

Right Touching and Wrong Touching

Now it is time to learn about Right Touching and Wrong Touching. In this chapter, you will learn more about how to be a member of the Sexual Abuse Prevention and Safety Team.

Right Touching is healthy and good touching. Right Touching is

when you ask before you touch and the other person says it's OK. Right Touching is when you ask for a hug, and the other person says OK. Right Touching is when you touch someone in a nice and caring way, in a place that is OK to touch. For example, shaking a person's hand when you meet them is a good example of Right Touching.

Right Touching is good and legal. You do not get in trouble for Right Touching. When something is *legal*, it is OK to do and you will not go to court or kids' jail if you do it.

Wrong Touching is when you touch a person in a mean or hurtful way. Wrong Touching is when you touch somebody else in their private parts without permission, even when you don't feel mean

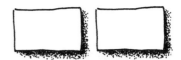

or you just want to share. Wrong Touching is when somebody else touches you in your private parts without your permission.

Wrong Touching is when you touch a person's private parts, and the person is more than 2 years younger than you, or if the other person is not as smart as you, or if you have to promise to give them money or a present to get them to do it. It is also Wrong Touching if the people doing the touching are too young to really understand all about what they are doing. It's Wrong Touching if you make the other person feel scared that you will hurt them if they don't do what you want. It's also Wrong Touching when you touch private parts with somebody in your family.

Wrong Touching is illegal! When something is *illegal,* it is against the law and that means it is not OK. When something is illegal, you can go to court or go to kids' jail for doing it. When something is illegal, it is a crime to do it. That means you might get in big trouble if you do something illegal. Things are illegal because they might hurt somebody. For example, it is illegal to steal money from someone. This is because people work hard for their money, and it hurts them and their families when people steal from them. It is illegal to drive too fast on the highway. It is illegal because a person who is driving too fast can hurt other people.

Think about how it feels inside when you want to do Wrong Touching. Maybe you feel like doing Wrong Touching because you have done it before. If you have done it before, then it might pop into your mind when you are doing something else. Other children might not have the idea pop up in their minds because they didn't

learn about Wrong Touching when they were younger. Other children might not be thinking about it, and they might not want to do Wrong Touching.

Remember, when you have sexual feelings, it doesn't mean that other people are having them too. They are your feelings. Your sexual feelings are not bad or wrong, but acting them out can get you in trouble and hurt other people.

Wrong Touching is illegal, or against the law, and in *Roadmaps*, you will be learning how to make good choices that will keep you out of trouble.

Sometimes doing Wrong Touching feels very good for a little while. Wrong Touching can make the person doing it feel strong, powerful, or sexy.

Sometimes people don't understand why they should try to stop doing Wrong Touching. Here are some reasons that other young boys and girls came up with:

Why Should I Stop Wrong Touching?

1. I might get in trouble with my teacher.
2. Other kids will pick on me.
3. Other kids will tease me.
4. Other kids will hate me.
5. Other kids won't play with me.
6. I will get in trouble with my parents.
7. I might get in trouble with my treatment group.

8. I might get arrested by the police.

9. I might go to kids' jail.

10. It might hurt the other person.

Now you have learned about what bad things might happen if you don't stop doing Wrong Touching. Here are some good things that might happen if you do stop doing Wrong Touching and only do Right Touching.

Good Things That Might Happen When You Stop Doing Wrong Touching

1. People will like you better, and you will have more friends.

2. It feels good to treat other people nicely.

3. Your counselor will think you're doing well in counseling and will give you more play time.

4. Your parents will be proud of you.

5. Your teachers will be proud of you.

6. You will not go to kids' jail.

7. People won't think you are weird or strange.

8. You won't be afraid of getting into trouble as much.

9. You won't have to go to court and talk to a judge.

10. You won't grow up to be a sex offender! (A *sex offender* is any person who does Wrong Sexual Touching that is illegal. A sex offender is someone who has gone to court, and a judge has decided that their sexual touching behavior was wrong enough to be called a sex offense.)

Assignment 4A

Now it is your turn to talk about your own reasons for stopping your Wrong Touching. In the space below, list some of your reasons for **not** doing any more Wrong Touching:

1. _____

2. _____

3. _____

4. _____

5. _____

Now, let's see how this works in real life. This next part of *Roadmaps* is to help you decide what is Right Touching and what is Wrong Touching.

Roadmaps will help you learn to stop behavior that hurts other people. Keep up the good work!

Assignment 4B

For each sentence, decide whether it is Right Touching or Wrong Touching. Check the best answer and tell your counselor why you chose it.

1. Your dad gives you a hug when you see him.
   ❏ Right Touching   ❏ Wrong Touching

2. You run up to people when you see them and surprise them by jumping on them.
   ❏ Right Touching   ❏ Wrong Touching

3. You touch your sister's private parts with your private part.
   ❏ Right Touching   ❏ Wrong Touching

4. You shake hands with your counselor when you see him.
   ❏ Right Touching   ❏ Wrong Touching

5. You hit people to see how they will react to you.
   ❏ Right Touching   ❏ Wrong Touching

6. Your mom rubs your back when you are tired.
   ❏ Right Touching   ❏ Wrong Touching

7. Your older sister had you put your penis in her private part.
   ❏ Right Touching   ❏ Wrong Touching

8. Sometimes you touch your private parts when you are around other people.
   ❏ Right Touching   ❏ Wrong Touching

Assignment 4B (continued)

9. A grownup put his mouth on your private part.
   ❑ Right Touching   ❑ Wrong Touching

10. Sometimes you kiss your boyfriend or girlfriend after asking if it is OK.
   ❑ Right Touching   ❑ Wrong Touching

11. Sometimes you rub your private parts in front of your brother.
   ❑ Right Touching   ❑ Wrong Touching

12. Sometimes you rub your private parts against someone when you are wrestling or playing.
   ❑ Right Touching   ❑ Wrong Touching

13. Your baby-sitter asks you to touch her private parts and you do.
   ❑ Right Touching   ❑ Wrong Touching

Great job! Take a break for a minute. Your counselor might have other examples like these that you can practice thinking about. By learning the difference between Right Touching and Wrong Touching, you will have a much happier life!

Assignment 4C

Almost everybody does some Right Touching and some Wrong Touching as they grow up. Write down 5 examples of Right Touching that you have done in your life.

1. _____

2. _____

3. _____

4. _____

5. _____

Assignment 4D

Now write down 5 examples of Wrong Touching that you have done in your life.

1. _____

2. _____

3. _____

4. _____

5. _____

Terrific! By writing these down and telling the truth, you are using Right Thinking! You will learn about Right Thinking in chapter 5.

Good Work! This was a hard Chapter! Now you are ready for Road Test 4.

ROAD TEST 4

Right Touching and Wrong Touching
(open book)

Name:_____

Date:_____

13 points possible. 12 points needed for passing.

Total Score:___/13   ❑ Pass   ❑ Need more work

1. Asking an adult for a hug is: (1 point)
     ❑ Right Touching   ❑ Wrong Touching

2. Wrong Touching means: (1 point)

        A. ____having poor table manners

        B. ____not combing your hair

        C. ____touching somebody without their permission

        D. ____not brushing your teeth

3. Check all of the things on this list that you think are touching or sexual behavior problems. (5 points)

    ❑ Touching your own private parts in public

    ❑ Shaking hands with your counselor

    ❑ Spying on other people who are undressing

    ❑ Talking too much about body parts in public

    ❑ Touching the private parts of a younger brother or sister

    ❑ Grabbing someone's bottom

    ❑ Asking someone for a hug

    ❑ Watching a movie that shows people kissing

4. You can control your sexual touching with another person. (1 point)
    ❑ True   ❑ False

For questions 5–7, read each scene and decide if it is Right Touching or Wrong Touching.

5. Jenny feels happy when she sees her counselor. When Jenny meets her counselor, she shakes her hand and says hello. (1 point)

❑ Right Touching   ❑ Wrong Touching

6. A.J. likes his counselor, and when he goes to his office, he sits very close to him and starts touching the counselor's arms and legs. (1 point)

❑ Right Touching   ❑ Wrong Touching

7. Billie asks his foster mother for a hug. She says OK. (1 point)

❑ Right Touching   ❑ Wrong Touching

8. What have you learned from reading this fourth chapter in *Roadmaps*? (2 points)

_____

_____

_____

Good job! Now you can fill in your progress chart and get a sticker or a high-five for chapter 4.

CHAPTER 5

Right Thinking and Wrong Thinking

Lots of boys and girls with touching problems worry that something is wrong with them that can never be fixed. This is just not so. Nobody is born with a touching problem. Most boys and girls with touching problems start their lives in a normal way just like other boys and girls. Boys and girls with touching problems usually learned about Wrong Touching when they saw other people do it, or when someone else did it to them.

In *Roadmaps* you are learning many new ways to change your behavior. One of the most important things you are learning is how to *think* differently. All human behavior starts in the brain. So when we pay attention to how our brains work, we can learn to change our behavior.

In this chapter, you will learn about Right Thinking and Wrong Thinking. You will learn to use your brain to think and act in new ways.

Right Thinking is when you are thinking in a healthy, good way. Right Thinking is when you are thinking ahead and thinking about what you are doing. Right Thinking is when you are taking responsibility for your choices and your behavior. Right Thinking is

> Learning to think differently helps you learn to act differently! You can do it! You are a good person who is learning new things!

when you are admitting what you have done. Right Thinking is when you are telling the truth.

Wrong Thinking is when you blame other people for your behavior. Wrong Thinking is when you lie about what you have done. Wrong Thinking is when you ignore how something hurts other people. Wrong Thinking is when you are being selfish. Wrong Thinking is when you ignore that something is illegal, or against the law. Wrong Thinking is when you don't think ahead, and you don't think about what might happen.

Do you know why you are learning about Right Thinking and Wrong Thinking? It is because you are a human being! Human beings use their brains and their thoughts to control their bodies. That means that—yes, you might have guessed it—Right Thinking leads to Right Touching, and Wrong Thinking leads to Wrong Touching.

If you can learn now about Right Thinking, you will have a much easier time staying out of trouble in the future.

There is another word for Wrong Thinking. Wrong Thinking is also called *Thinking Errors*. A Thinking Error is like a thinking mistake. So, Wrong Thinking is like making a mistake in your head. Wrong Thinking is like taking the wrong road somewhere and getting lost or stuck in a dead end or even going off a cliff!

There are many different kinds of Thinking Errors. Here is a list of some basic Thinking Errors:

Whoaaaaa! I better pay attention and use my brakes or else I am going to be in BIG trouble!

Anger: This is when you express your feelings by showing anger, instead of talking about the other feelings you are having. For example, Cougar gets made fun of by other kids. Instead of talking about it or asking for help from a teacher, he goes up to one of the other kids and hits him in the face, giving him a black eye. He then gets suspended from school. This is *anger*.

Blaming: This is when you blame someone else for something that you have done. For example, Bob steals something from Phil and then says that Tammy did the stealing. This is *blaming*.

Excuse making: This is when you make up excuses for your behavior. This is when you say that you did something because of something else. Another name for this Thinking Error is **Justifying.** For example, Russ doesn't turn in his homework. When

the teacher asks him about it, he says, "I was trapped in my room surrounded by wild boars, and to satisfy their hunger I fed them my homework, and they ran off in a stampede." This is *excuse making*.

Lack of Empathy: This is when you only think about yourself, and you ignore how your behavior will affect other people. Another name for this Thinking Error is **Me, Me, Me.** This Thinking Error is all about being selfish and not thinking about others. For example, Ruth is rude—she goes around to other kids and talks about how they don't dress very well. This is *lack of empathy*.

Lying: This is when you say you did not do something that you really did do. For example, George hit Zack. When Zack told on him, George said that he didn't do it. This is *lying*.

Minimizing: This is when you make a wrong behavior seem less wrong than it really was. This is when you make a mistake seem small by only admitting to a small part of what happened. Words like *only, just,* and *but* are warning signs that you might be using this Thinking Error. For example, Teresa broke her parents' lamp by throwing it on the floor when she was mad. When asked about it, Teresa said, "But I only touched it a little, and it just fell off the table." This is *minimizing*.

Never, ever, always: This is when a person uses words like *never, ever,* or *always.* Another word for this Thinking Error is **Universals** or **All-or-nothing thinking.** Sometimes people exaggerate in order to make their point. For example, a girl says to her mother, "You never let me do what I want." Another example is when a boy says to his father, "You always believe John instead of me." Don't you hate it when your parents say that you never pick up your clothes? The truth is that you probably did pick up your clothes at least once in the last 5 years! This is *never, ever, always.*

Leonard is 11 years old. He has learned about Wrong Thinking, or Thinking Errors. Leonard says:

If you have done something wrong, and you blame someone else for your behavior, that is a Thinking Error.

If you are thinking about doing some sexual touching with a much younger person, then that is a Thinking Error, even if you haven't done the Wrong Touching yet.

If you think that people are always picking on you, that's a Thinking Error because you aren't helpless. You can do some positive things to make any situation better.

If you get in trouble for something and decide to lie about it so you don't get caught, then that's a Thinking Error. It is best to be honest and admit to what you have done.

Tucker is 7 years old and is trying to learn to control his body and behavior. Tucker explains what he is learning about Right Thinking. Tucker says:

> Right Thinking is when you tell the truth. Right Thinking is when you admit to something you did wrong. Right Thinking is when you think about other people, not just yourself.
> Wrong Thinking is when you tell a lie. Wrong Thinking is when you only think about yourself. Wrong Thinking is when you blame other people.

Keenan, who is 9, is using Right Thinking because he is admitting to his mistakes. Listen to how brave he is:

I was 8 when I did it. I feel guilty for what I did. I did some Wrong Touching with my younger sisters, who were 6 and 7. I felt sad when I got caught. I guess I didn't want to get caught. Now I am glad that I am getting help so that I will not have to go to jail.

Here are some more examples of Right Thinking:

Thinking of how you can help other people, instead of acting selfishly.

Thinking of being a good friend.

Deciding to let someone else go first at something.

Deciding to share something (but **not** your private parts!) rather than keep it to yourself.

Telling the whole truth about something you did.

Talking about what makes you worry.

Thinking ahead instead of acting on impulse.

Keeping a comment to yourself if it might hurt another person.

Talking about your feelings rather than just getting mad.

Thinking about what you did wrong, rather than blaming what happened on someone else.

Doing a chore right now, instead of acting lazy and telling yourself that you can do it later.

Assignment 5A

One of the best ways to learn to stay out of trouble is to always use Right Thinking. Give 4 examples of when you used Right Thinking during the past week or 2. You can ask your counselor or parents for help with this.

1. _____

2. _____

3. _____

4. _____

Assignment 5B

Read each sentence below and decide if it is Right Thinking or Wrong Thinking. Check your answer. Your counselor or parents can help if you need it.

1. Ricky tells his foster mother, "You are right, I did make a mess in my room."

       ❑ Right Thinking   ❑ Wrong Thinking

Assignment 5B (continued)

2. Mary tells her mother that she did touch her little sister in her private parts. (This one could be hard to decide because Mary did Wrong Touching. Is telling the truth about it Right Thinking or Wrong Thinking?)

     ❑ Right Thinking   ❑ Wrong Thinking

3. Jeanne tells her friend Rosa, "It's OK if you want to play with my Nintendo Wii. I will play with my X-Box."

     ❑ Right Thinking   ❑ Wrong Thinking

4. John tells his father, "It is all your fault that I didn't do my chores."

     ❑ Right Thinking   ❑ Wrong Thinking

5. Leroy always feels like people are mean to him, so he thinks it is OK to call them names to get back at them.

     ❑ Right Thinking   ❑ Wrong Thinking

6. Mrs. King, the teacher, blames Bruce for losing a book, and then she finds the book in her car.

     ❑ Right Thinking   ❑ Wrong Thinking

7. Ten-year-old Shawn has touching problems and doesn't have many friends his age. He thinks that he might as well play with the little kids, the 5-year-olds, since they like him.

     ❑ Right Thinking   ❑ Wrong Thinking

Assignment 5B (continued)

8. Kimberly's mother asks her to clean her room. Kimberly keeps promising that she will do it later, after she finishes her video game.

❑ Right Thinking   ❑ Wrong Thinking

9. Donnie is upset about his family not visiting. He feels like running away, but he decides to talk to his counselor instead because he might feel better if he talks to someone.

❑ Right Thinking   ❑ Wrong Thinking

Great job! If there were some you didn't understand, ask your counselor or group for help.

Now you can learn another new word. The word is *denial*. When you lie or don't tell the whole truth about something, that's denial. Denial can also mean pretending something is not happening. Denial is like a Roadblock in your way to getting where you are going.

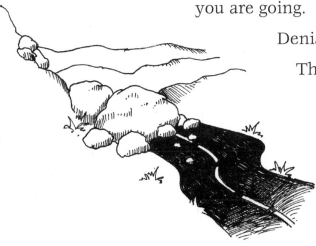

Denial is another type of Wrong Thinking.

Here's Amber, who is 11, talking about why she denied her wrong behaviors at the beginning of treatment.

I felt shy because I don't like talking about things that happened in the past. I especially don't like talking about sexual things because they make me feel squirmy inside. I have learned that I was in denial. Now I talk about my sexual behaviors because I have learned that it is OK to talk about them. I have learned that I am not a bad person, and it is OK to talk about my mistakes.

Lots of people use denial to cover up their mistakes so they will not get in trouble. Some adults use denial too. A lie is a type of denial. When you lie you are denying the truth.

Look at the cartoon to the right. The girl in the cartoon says she hasn't seen any candy, but the truth is that she's eating it right now! That is an example of one kind of denial.

To get very far in *Roadmaps,* it is important for you to stop denying what you have done in the past and tell the whole truth. When you do, you will have a good life and learn from the mistakes you have made.

Here is an assignment to help you stop using denial. You may want to ask your counselor, parent, foster parent, or a group home staff member to help you with this assignment.

Assignment 5C

List 3 mistakes that you have told the truth about in the last month. For example, "I did take the quarter from the table"; "I did break the lamp"; "I did kick the dog"; "I did not turn in my homework."

1. _____

2. _____

3. _____

Now list 3 things that you lied about in the last month. It doesn't matter if you got caught in the lie or not. You may write any kind of lie you've told. For example, "I said I fed the dog when I didn't"; "I said I took a shower when I didn't"; "I said I didn't have any homework when I did"; "I said I ate all my vegetables when I gave them to my rabbit."

1. _____

2. _____

3. _____

Denial is not for me. It's just a Roadblock in my way!

In *Roadmaps* it is important to tell the whole truth. The faster you can overcome your denial, the more successful you will be.

Another kind of Right Thinking and Wrong Thinking is what we tell ourselves inside our heads. In *Roadmaps* we call this positive and negative self-talk. *Self-talk* is what you say to yourself inside your own head. You don't actually talk out loud; you just think it.

Positive self-talk is Right Thinking, because we are saying good things to ourselves. Positive self-talk means to talk to yourself inside your head and tell yourself positive, helpful things. For example, "I am smart and I am friendly" is positive self-talk. Another example of positive self-talk is, "I am doing the best I can, and I will do it right soon." Another example is, "It is OK to make some mistakes. At least I am learning to do better."

Negative self-talk is Wrong Thinking, because we are saying bad or mean things to ourselves. Negative self-talk is when you say things like, "I am so dumb, I will never do anything right." Another example is, "I am

POSITIVE SELF-TALK

I am learning new skills, even if I make a mistake, I am a smart and friendly person.

not very good-looking, so nobody will like me." Negative self-talk is Wrong Thinking, and you should tell your brain to stop doing it.

Guess what? You can tell your brain to stop using negative self-talk or any kind of Wrong Thinking. Sometimes it is as easy as learning about Right Thinking and Wrong Thinking. Now that you know that Wrong Thinking leads to Wrong Touching, you can decide to stop using Wrong Thinking. It can be very easy. Just try it. Change your thinking around. When you feel like

you are not very good at something, just start telling yourself something that you are good at. For example, "I have good manners, and I am a friendly person" are simple things to tell yourself.

> *I have a strong body, and a strong motor. I can get through the worst road.*

Assignment 5D

Let's practice some positive self-talk. In the space below, list 3 things you like about yourself. Nobody will argue with you—this is your list. Write down 3 things that you think are good and healthy about you.

1. _____

2. _____

3. _____

Now you are on the right road. You are learning to use positive self-talk, which is Right Thinking. Your brain is working the right way now. Even very smart people sometimes make mistakes, and in this chapter you have learned to tell the truth, even when you have done something wrong. That is another big step toward becoming a Survivor! You have learned about Thinking Errors, and you have learned to fix those Thinking Errors by using Right Thinking! You have also learned that your brain is in charge of all of your behavior, and that you can change how your brain works by using positive self-talk. Now it is time to see how much of this you can remember. Good luck on Road Test 5—you will do a great job!

Right Thinking and Wrong Thinking
(open book)

Name:_____

Date:_____

12 points possible. 11 points needed for passing.

Total Score:___/12   ❑ Pass   ❑ Need more work

1. Check all the things on this list that are examples of Right Thinking. (2 points)

    ❑ Telling the truth about a mistake

    ❑ Keeping a toy to yourself, and never sharing it with others

    ❑ Blaming your mistake on someone else

    ❑ Offering to help someone else, even though you are busy

    ❑ Lying about a problem to save yourself from being embarrassed

2. Wrong Thinking leads to Wrong Touching. (1 point)
    ❑ True   ❑ False

3. Right Thinking leads to Right Touching. (1 point)
    ❑ True   ❑ False

4. Wrong Thinking leads to Right Touching. (1 point)
   ❑ True   ❑ False

5. Right Thinking leads to Wrong Touching. (1 point)
   ❑ True   ❑ False

6. Denial is one type of Right Thinking. (1 point)
   ❑ True   ❑ False

7. When you lie or don't tell the whole truth about something, it is called: (1 point)

   A. ____withholding evidence.

   B. ____Right Thinking.

   C. ____denial.

   D. ____reoffending.

8. To succeed in *Roadmaps*, you need to: (1 point)

   A. ____tell some of the truth.

   B. ____tell the truth every other day.

   C. ____tell the whole truth, all the time.

   D. ____keep the truth to yourself, because it is
        personal and private.

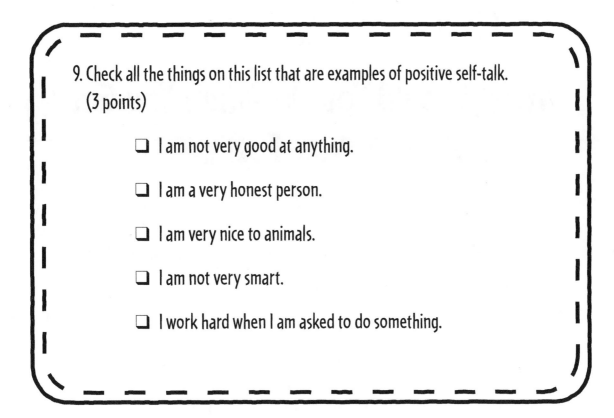

9. Check all the things on this list that are examples of positive self-talk. (3 points)

❑ I am not very good at anything.

❑ I am a very honest person.

❑ I am very nice to animals.

❑ I am not very smart.

❑ I work hard when I am asked to do something.

Good work on this test and this chapter! Get a sticker or a high-five from your counselor and mark your progress in your progress chart.

CHAPTER 6

What Should You Do When You Get Those Sexual Feelings?

Sexual feelings happen to everyone. Children, teenagers, and adults all have sexual feelings, or *urges,* though not always in the same ways.

As you grow up and your body changes in puberty, you might find that you have more and more sexual thoughts and feelings, or sexual urges. In *puberty* your body is helping you get ready to be a young man or young woman. Hair grows under your arms and on your private area. If you are a boy, your voice might get deeper. If you are a girl, your breasts start to grow and you may begin your monthly cycle, called *menstruation* (say men-strew-AY-shun), when you start to bleed a little from your vagina. In chapter 7, "Understanding and Caring for Your Changing Body," you will learn more about the many changes that come with puberty.

In *Roadmaps* you never have to be afraid or ashamed of your sexual feelings. In *Roadmaps* it is good to talk with your counselor, parent, or foster parent about your sexual feelings. What is **not** OK is to act on those feelings with Wrong Touching. You can't get into trouble for having sexual feelings, but you can get into trouble for doing Wrong Touching.

Here are some ideas that Jacob, 9, came up with. He has been learning how to control his sexual feelings and urges:

I have learned that masturbation is OK. Masturbation for boys is when you rub your penis. I have learned that it can make you feel good without hurting other people. I have learned that it is best to masturbate in private when nobody else is watching you.

When I get urges to do sexual touching I tell myself to calm down. I also do fun things like sports to keep my mind off it. Sometimes when I am really worried about doing Wrong Touching, I tell an adult. I also think about what might happen in the future if I do Wrong Touching. When I think about getting into trouble, I stop my sexual urges.

Girls get sexual feelings just like boys do. Girls also touch their private parts, and it is also called masturbation. *Masturbation* is a private activity that boys and girls should do in a private place like a bedroom with the door closed.

Here is a list of 10 things you can do to help yourself control your sexual urges.

1. Go tell an adult.

2. Masturbate in private.

3. Play a game to get your mind off of it.

4. Tell your brain to stop, and think about what might happen in the future if you can't control your sexual urges.

5. Get some hard physical exercise to wear yourself out.

6. Do 50 sit-ups in your bedroom.

7. Quickly get away from any younger children.

8. Think about how awful it would be to go to kids' jail.

9. Think about how other people would feel disappointed in you if you did Wrong Touching.

10. Yell "no!" inside your head, and do something else.

Assignment 6A

List all of the people that you feel safe enough with to talk to about your sexual feelings and masturbation.

1. _____

2. _____

3. _____

4. _____

5. _____

Assignment 6B

Now pick 1 of the people from your list. Talk to that person about your sexual feelings this week. You might want to ask the person what ideas they have about controlling sexual feelings.

Person's Name: _____

Have the other person write down what you said and then sign this paper.

What I said: _____

_____

_____

_____

Signature: _____

Assignment 6C

List 3 things that work for you to help control your sexual feelings.

1. _____

2. _____

3. _____

Remember, everybody gets sexual feelings as they grow older. Sexual feelings are not bad—they are perfectly normal.

It is your job to learn how to control your sexual feelings so that you don't hurt other people, and so that you don't get into trouble.

What Should You Do When You Get Those Sexual Feelings?
(open book)

Name:_____

Date:_____

9 points possible. 8 points needed for passing.

Total Score:___/9   ❑ Pass   ❑ Need more work

1. Check all the behaviors on this list that are healthy ways to handle sexual feelings. (5 points)

❑ Exercise

❑ Read

❑ Play a video game

❑ Watch a porno movie

❑ Touch someone's privates to get the feeling out

❑ Sleep in the same room with your younger brother or sister

❑ Distract yourself by thinking of something that is not sexual

❑ Distract yourself by starting a fight with a friend

❑ Stare at a person's private parts until the feeling goes away

❑ Ask a stranger for sex

❑ Write my sexual feelings in my diary

2. Sexual feelings happen to everyone. (1 point)
    ❏ True   ❏ False

3. When puberty starts, your body changes in many ways. (1 point)
    ❏ True   ❏ False

4. Sexual feelings are always bad. (1 point)
    ❏ True   ❏ False

5. Masturbation is something that both boys and girls do sometimes. (1 point)
    ❏ True   ❏ False

Great job on this test and on this chapter! Get a sticker or a high-five from your counselor and mark your progress in your progress chart.

CHAPTER 7

Understanding and Caring for Your Changing Body

A lot of you who are reading *Roadmaps* have something very important to look forward to. That important thing is called *puberty*. Some of you may be going through puberty now. And some of you may already have been through puberty. In this chapter, you will learn about how bodies work so that you will better understand how to stay safe and healthy as you grow up. This chapter will help you understand and feel comfortable with your changing body.

As boys and girls get to be between 10 and 13 years old, their bodies start to change. This change is called *puberty*. Puberty is the time when your body changes from a child's body to a more adult-like body. Some boys and girls start puberty earlier than age 10 and some start later than age 13. It's all a normal part of growing up.

Buzzbee has a word of advice for you here. He knows that many boys and girls get very excited reading this chapter, and that seeing drawings of bodies can lead to sexual feelings. Those feelings are normal.

If your sexual feelings get too strong, take a break, tell your counselor, and get some exercise.

During puberty, your body grows very fast, and many changes happen. The main thing you will see is that body hair starts growing under your arms and around your private parts. Girls may notice that their breasts are starting to grow bigger. Boys' penises start to get larger, and both boys and girls develop more muscles. Boys will grow hair on their faces later during puberty. Boys' voices get deeper during

Girl's body: 5 stages of puberty

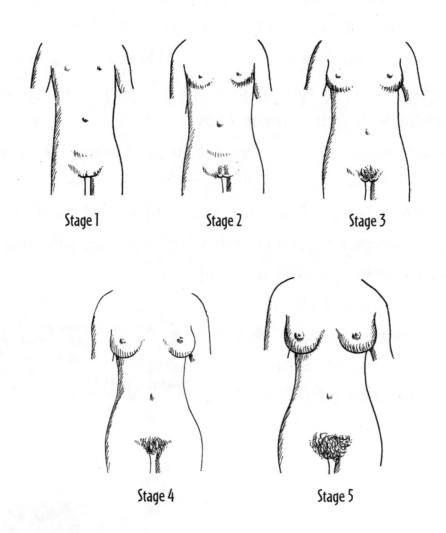

Stage 1   Stage 2   Stage 3

Stage 4   Stage 5

puberty. Other changes are going on inside that you can't see. This is an important time!

The pictures below show how your body will change as you go through puberty. Notice that there are five stages of puberty. Which stage are you in now?

Boy's body: 5 stages of puberty

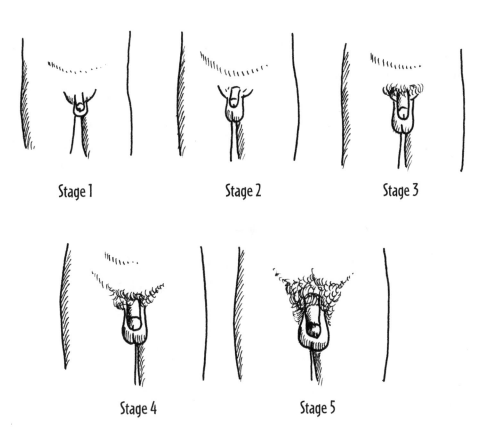

Stage 1   Stage 2   Stage 3

Stage 4   Stage 5

Some boys wonder why their penis looks different from the penis of another boy. Of course, the private parts of boys and girls all look somewhat different, just like the rest of our bodies look somewhat different. Many years ago, most boys had the *foreskin* (say "4-skin") trimmed off the end of their penis soon after they were born. This is called *circumcision* (say "SIR-cum-si-zhun"). People used to believe that this was a good idea to help boys keep their penises clean; and for some families, it is part of their religion. Now many parents are choosing to leave the foreskin, because it is easy for a boy to keep his penis clean as long as he pays attention to it. Many parents still choose circumcision for their sons, either because they think it is healthier or because of their religious beliefs. This is one reason why some penises look different. Below are 2 drawings—one of a circumcised penis, and one of a penis that is not circumcised.

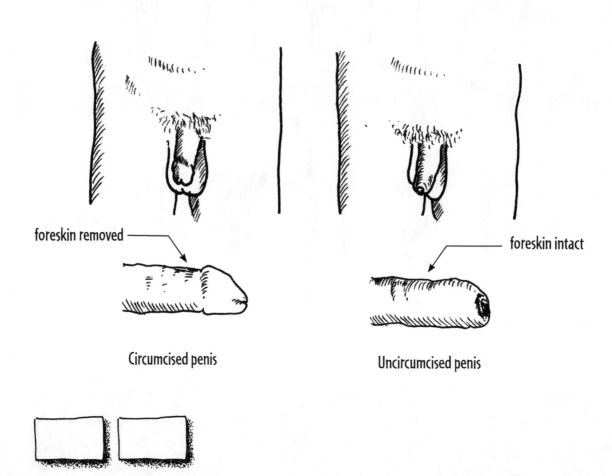

foreskin removed

foreskin intact

Circumcised penis

Uncircumcised penis

During puberty, boys start making *sperm*. Sperm is what swims up inside a girl or woman and joins with an egg to make a baby. Sperm is made in the testicles. Boys make sperm their whole lives, so they never run out. Sperm are very small. It takes a microscope to see them. Sperm comes out when a boy or man *ejaculates* (say "ee-JAK-yew-lates") during masturbation or sex, or during a "wet dream" that happens while sleeping.

Masturbation is when a boy touches or rubs his penis or a girl touches or rubs her *clitoris* (say "CLIT-or-is") and vulva and it feels very good.

A girl's clitoris sits under a little hood at the top of where the lips of her private parts come together. It's about the size of a small button and is very sensitive to touch and can make a girl feel all excited inside. This is a good time to explain 2 other words. One of those words is *vagina*. Only girls have vaginas. Vaginas are where babies come out of the body when they are born. Sometimes the vagina is called a girl's inside private part, because it is inside the body. The *vulva* is the girl's outside private part. The vulva is all of the skin and body parts that protect the opening to the vagina.

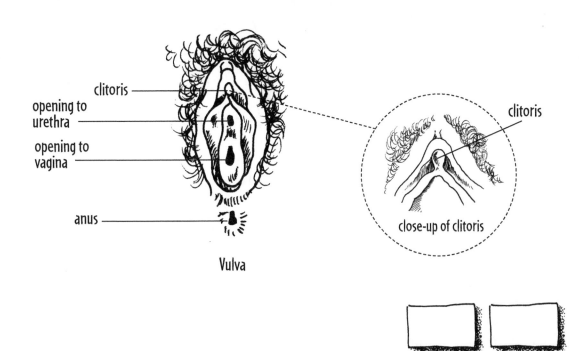

clitoris

opening to urethra

opening to vagina

anus

Vulva

clitoris

close-up of clitoris

Every girl is born with hundreds of thousands of eggs inside her body in a place called her *ovary*. All girls have 2 ovaries. When a girl gets to puberty, her body starts to make 1 of her eggs ripe every month. Girls know this is happening when they start having monthly periods. All through the month, their bodies have been busy using blood and other matter to make a home for an egg to grow in. If the egg doesn't need its home that month, it drains out from a girl's vagina. That monthly period is also called *menstruation* (say "men-strew-AY-shun").

Inside a girl's private area

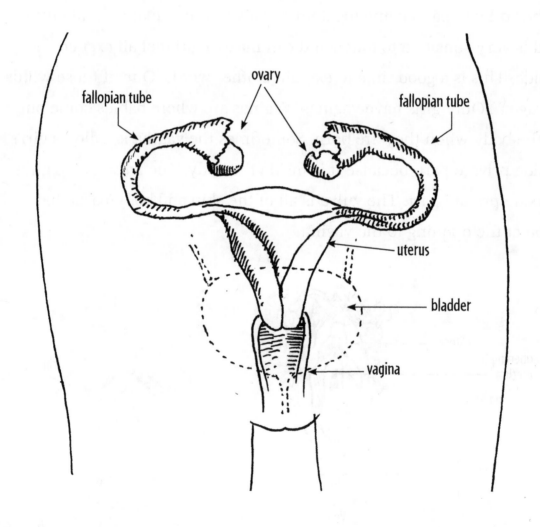

An egg only needs the new home if a man's sperm swims up inside and joins with the woman's egg. If that happens, the egg is fertilized. A fertilized egg attaches to the cushion of blood, and a baby starts growing. This happens after a man and a woman have sex. During sex, the man's penis goes into the woman's vagina, and sperm from the man's penis is released into the vagina. From the vagina the sperm swim up and try to find the woman's egg. If that happens, a baby starts growing inside the woman. Babies take 9 months to grow large enough to be born.

Inside a boy's private area

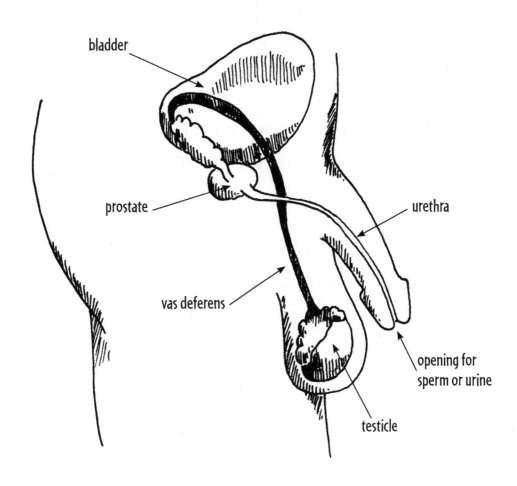

Go ahead and take a break here. When you and your counselor are ready, come back and start again right here.

Welcome back. There are a few more things *Roadmaps* would like you to know about boys' and girls' private parts. There are some diseases and infections that people get mainly from doing sexual touching. These diseases and infections are called *STDs* (*sexually transmitted diseases*) or *STIs* (*sexually transmitted infections*). In *Roadmaps* you have learned that sometimes sexual touching is illegal, or against the law, and people can get into big trouble for doing it. It is also important to know that it is very common for people to get these special types of diseases and infections from doing private part touching with other persons. Sometimes the diseases are very serious, like HIV, AIDS, and herpes. Sometimes the infections just cause scratching and itching,

like an infection of crabs, which are little tiny bugs that can live around your private parts.

Because there are many different types of STDs and STIs, most people believe that it is a good idea to wait to do sexual touching with other people until you are older, and you know all about how to prevent all the different diseases and infections that you might catch.

Bodies are very special and wonderful things, and if you make good choices, your body will bring you lots of fun and exciting times, including sex. By understanding how your body works, you won't have to feel worried or ashamed about the things you feel in your body.

You can also see why our bodies are private, and why each person has a right to decide his or her own body boundaries. A *body boundary* is a person's private space, like how much room you want around you. When people get too close to us, we say that they are in our boundaries or in our space.

It is also up to you to show that you are in charge of your own body. You can show this by being healthy and clean and taking good care of your body.

Assignment 7A

Some of the ways healthy people take care of themselves are listed in this chart. As you read the list, put a check mark in the first column next to the things you already do to care for yourself and a check mark in the second column next to the things you need to work on.

Personal Care Task	I do this	I need to work on this
Bathe or shower every day		
Wash my hair with shampoo when I bathe or shower		
Brush my teeth twice a day		
Comb my hair		
Wear clean clothes every day		
Put on deodorant every day		
Change my underwear every day		
Trim and clean my fingernails when I need to		
Wash my hands after going to the bathroom		
Change my socks every day		
Blow my nose with a tissue, not my hand		
Put away my clean and dirty clothes in the right places		

Talk to your counselor and your treatment group (if you have one) about how you take care of yourself. Gently remind others in your group if they need to work harder on keeping clean and healthy. Use the chart on the next page if you need to work on some things like these. Your counselor will help you fill out the chart, and you can then have your parents, foster parents, or group home staff sign it every day to help you remember to do those things.

Assignment 7B

Weekly Behavior Chart

Use this chart to change daily behavior patterns to stay on the road to a healthy life. Pick areas to work on from the Personal Care Task list, or pick other behaviors. Add new goals as you achieve the first ones. Have an adult sign the box for each day.

Behavior to work on	Mon	Tues	Wed	Thurs	Fri	Sat	Sun

Sometimes looking healthy also means respecting your body and other people in public by keeping yourself from doing things that might embarrass you, your family, or your friends.

Here are some tips:

1. Blow your nose with a tissue—don't pick it.

2. Try not to suck on your fingers, toes, pencils, erasers, or sleeves (try a peppermint instead).

3. Keep your feet off the furniture.

4. Keep your hands in Right Touching places.

5. Zip up your pants zipper all the way all the time (except when you are using the bathroom).

6. Speak clearly—not too loud, not too soft.

7. Quietly say, "Excuse me" when you pass gas. Try to move away from other people when you do it.

8. Don't joke about other people's bodies. Everyone wants to like their own body. Respect that!

9. Be friendly, but respect other people's boundaries. If you want to have friends, be friendly not pushy.

ROAD TEST
7

Understanding and Caring
for Your Changing Body
(closed book)

Name:_____

Date:_____

19 points possible. 17 points needed for passing.

Total Score:___/19   ❏ Pass   ❏ Need more work

1. Puberty only happens to girls. (1 point)

      ❏ True   ❏ False

2. The foreskin is part of a girl's private parts. (1 point)

      ❏ True   ❏ False

3. The clitoris is part of a girl's private area that: (1 point)

    A. ___feels good.

    B. ___babies come out of.

    C. ___urine comes out of.

    D. ___the girl's eggs develop in.

4. Menstruation is when: (1 point)

    A. ___boys become men after going through puberty.

    B. ___girls start to bleed every month.

    C. ___girls get too old to have babies.

    D. ___a girl gets pregnant.

    E. ___a girl rubs her private area.

5. For each item on the list below, indicate if it is found in a boy (B) or a girl (G) or both (Both). (12 points)

___ Eggs	___ Fallopian tubes
___ Foreskin	___ Ovary
___ Vulva	___ Sperm
___ Testicle	___ Uterus
___ Penis	___ Vagina
___ Breasts	___ Bladder

6. A girl gets pregnant when: (1 point)

    A. ___she has sex on the wrong day.

    B. ___she has sex with a very sexy boy.

    C. ___a sperm swims and joins with an egg in a girl.

    D. ___she goes on a date with a boy and lets the boy kiss her.

7. How are babies made? (2 points)

_____

_____

_____

_____

Great job on this test! Mark your progress on your progress chart and get a sticker or a high-five from your counselor!

CHAPTER 8

Learning to Control Your Body and Stay Out of Kids' Jail

Almost everywhere, children with sexual touching problems are given help so that they can learn to stop Wrong Sexual Touching and lead happy lives. But by about age 12, a child that doesn't stop Wrong Sexual Touching can get into serious trouble and go to kids' jail. In some places, kids can go to kids' jail when they are even younger, sometimes 8, 9, 10, or 11 years old.

Sandy is 11 and has been in counseling for about 6 months because of her touching problems. Here's what she has to say:

I had a lot of sexual problems, and I almost got put in kids' jail for them. I have touched other young kids in wrong ways. Sometimes it is hard for me to stop.

I know one thing for sure—I do not want to go to kids' jail. If you are reading this book, then you probably have some of the same problems I do. So, if you have sexual problems, you better learn to control them, or you might end up hearing a judge tell you you're going to jail.

Assignment 8A

In the space below, write 10 good reasons to stay out of kids' jail.
Think about it this way: Why do you want to stay out of kids' jail?

1. _____

2. _____

3. _____

4. _____

5. _____

6. _____

7. _____

8. _____

9. _____

10. _____

Now it is time to learn about some important words. A *court* is a big room with one important person in charge. That person is a *judge*. The judge has the job of deciding what kind of punishment a person should get when a person does something that is illegal, which means against the law. Judges have the right to give out lots of punishments, and the police have to follow what the judge says. If a judge tells a person to go to jail, the police will put the person in jail until the

judge says the person can get out. Kids don't get sent to regular jails, because it wouldn't be safe. So if a child does something that is against the law, a judge might send a child to counseling, or maybe to *kids' jail*. Another word for kids' jail is *juvie* or *juvenile detention*. *Juvenile detention* is a place with locked doors where a child has to live and follow strict rules until the judge says it is time to get out.

Most smart people try to avoid doing things that can lead to jail for kids or adults. If you never do anything that is illegal, or against the law, you will never have to hear a judge tell you to go to kids' jail. If you only do things that are legal, you will stay out of kids' jail.

Here are some rules about sexual touching that will help keep you out of kids' jail:

1. Never touch anybody in any way without getting permission first.

2. Never use force, threats, presents, or bribes to get someone to do sexual touching with you.

3. Never touch someone's private parts if they are more than 2 years younger than you are, even if they say it's OK.

4. Never talk to younger children about sex or personal body parts.

5. Never do sexual touching with family members.

6. Never touch your own private parts except when you are alone in a private place like your bedroom or the bathroom.

7. Never do anything that hurts another person.

Sometimes things that are wrong or unhealthy can still be legal. For example, it is legal to eat rotten food, but you will probably get sick. It might be legal to have sex when you are 13 years old, but it sure is **not** a good idea. So making sure something is legal should be only one part of your thinking. You should also want to make good, healthy choices. It's legal to eat worms and slugs, but is it a good idea? Probably not, unless you are starving to death in the woods. It's legal to paint purple stars all over your body, but is it a good idea? Probably not, unless you like people staring at you.

Sexual behavior is sometimes legal, even for young people within a certain age. In *Roadmaps* we want you to learn that sexual touching is a big responsibility, and if you make a mistake, you can go to kids'

jail, you can get pregnant or get someone else pregnant, or you can get a bad disease. Young people need to wait until they are old enough to really understand all of these things before they start doing sexual behavior with other people.

Let's look at the rules about sexual touching again and see what they mean in more detail.

1. **Never touch anybody in any way without getting permission first.**

   Now is a good time to learn an important word. That word is *consent*. *Consent* is when someone gives their permission to do something and that person really understands what is going to happen. Young children and some people with special problems don't really understand sexual touching and can't really give their consent. So sexual touching is probably against the law if the other person doesn't give permission and you touch the person's private parts anyway. It is also probably against the law if the other person is more than 2 years younger, or if they are someone with special problems and don't understand all about sex.

2. **Never use force, threats, presents, or bribes to get someone to do sexual touching with you.**

   It is illegal, or against the law, if you try to do sexual touching by giving the person presents or money. It is also against the law if you say that you will hurt the other person or break the person's toys. It is also against the law if you say that you will hurt the other person's pets, friends, or family members. Those are quick ways to end up in court or kids' jail for Wrong Touching.

3. **Never touch someone's private parts if they are more than 2 years younger than you are, even if they say it's OK.**

In most places, even young children can be arrested by the police. In some places, 8-year-olds can be arrested. In most places, sexual touching is against the law when the person doing the touching is more than 2 years older than the other person and when the other person is younger than 12 years old.

Some sexual touching can be OK, but only when both people want to do the touching, and when they are about the same age and they are old enough to really understand what they are doing. If you are more than 2 years older than someone you want to do sexual touching with, watch out, because it might be illegal, or against the law. Your counselor can teach you about the exact laws where you live.

4. **Never talk to younger children about sex or personal body parts.**

By talking to younger children about sexual behavior or personal body parts, you are teaching the child about sex and seeing if they are interested in sex. This is against the law in many places.

5. **Never do sexual touching with family members.**

Sexual behavior with family members is called *incest* and is against the law, as you learned in chapter 2, "What Is a Touching Problem?"

6. **Never touch your own private parts except when you are alone in a private place like your bedroom or the bathroom.**

All sexual behavior is private and should only be done in a private place where nobody else can see. It is illegal, or against the law, to do sexual touching or show your private parts in a public place where other people can see it.

7. **Never do anything that hurts another person.**

It is wrong to do things that hurt other people. It is almost always against the law to hurt other people. Sexual touching can sometimes feel good to one person but hurt the other person. In life, it is a good thing to always think about how your behavior affects others.

Now that you know and better understand the rules about sexual touching, here are some examples for you to think about. Decide if these behaviors are legal or illegal. Remember, if a behavior is illegal, or against the law, the person can be arrested by the police and might have to go to court or to kids' jail.

Assignment 8B

Check the right answer for each situation.

1. Mary is 9. Beth is her best friend's 5-year-old sister. Mary kisses Beth and touches her private parts while playing hide and seek.

     ❑ Legal   ❑ Illegal (Against the Law)

2. John is 10. One day he asks his 6-year-old friend, Josh, to show him his penis. Then John touches Josh's penis.

     ❑ Legal   ❑ Illegal (Against the Law)

3. Jasmine is 8. One day she tries to get her 4-year-old brother to touch her private parts.

     ❑ Legal   ❑ Illegal (Against the Law)

4. Anne is 10 years old. After school she asks an 11-year-old boy to give her a hug.

     ❑ Legal   ❑ Illegal (Against the Law)

5. Miguel is 11. While baby-sitting his 7-year-old cousin, he rubs his privates on his cousin's bottom.

     ❑ Legal   ❑ Illegal (Against the Law)

6. Jeremiah sometimes gets very mad. One day while at school, he grabs the private parts of another boy, hurting the other boy.

     ❑ Legal   ❑ Illegal (Against the Law)

7. Jonathon is 9 years old, and he asks a girl in his class, Jeannie, if he can kiss her. She says OK, and he kisses her.

     ❑ Legal   ❑ Illegal (Against the Law)

Assignment 8B (continued)

8. Bob is 10 years old. One day at school, he goes into the bathroom and shows his penis to other boys. The other boys don't want to see it.

    ❑ Legal   ❑ Illegal (Against the Law)

9. Monica lives in a foster home and is 12 years old. One day while walking home from school, she asks her 12-year-old friend, Deon, if she can kiss him. He says OK, so they kiss.

    ❑ Legal   ❑ Illegal (Against the Law)

10. Patrick is 11 years old. One day at school, he walks up behind a female teacher and grabs her bottom with his hand.

    ❑ Legal   ❑ Illegal (Against the Law)

Great job! You are learning a lot! Follow the rules about sexual touching, and you will stay out of trouble and live a happy and successful life!

Your counselor will help you figure out if your answers were right or wrong. Don't worry if you missed some of the right answers. The point is to learn about this stuff now so you don't grow up with wrong ideas that get you in trouble!

Some kids with touching problems have other problems with controlling their bodies as well. It's important to work on these problems too. In *Roadmaps* you are learning to control your body in good ways at all times. You are

learning about Right Body Control and Right Thinking. Once again, you are learning that your brain is very important, since your brain controls all your behavior.

Manny is in counseling for doing sexual behavior with his sisters. One day at school, he gets into an argument with Jordan. Manny calls Jordan a name, and then he hits Jordan. Jordan gets mad and tries to choke Manny. Manny then grabs some scissors and chases Jordan. When the teachers break up the fight, they suspend Manny from school for chasing Jordan with scissors.

Manny was mad at first that the teachers suspended him and not Jordan, because he thought he was right and that Jordan had started the argument. When he talked with his counselor, he realized that he was using Wrong Thinking, and that he wasn't controlling his body in

a good way. His brain was working in the same mixed-up way it was when he abused his sisters.

Like Manny, you are learning new and better ways to control your body.

Assignment 8C

Write down 5 times you did not control your body as well as you should have during the past 2 weeks. These would be times when you used Wrong Thinking, and the Wrong Thinking led to you doing some wrong behavior. (Examples: not doing a chore, calling someone a name, hitting someone, breaking something, acting lazy, etc.)

1. _____

2. _____

3. _____

4. _____

5. _____

Assignment 8D

Now write down 5 times that you controlled your body in a good way during the past 2 weeks. These would be times when you used Right Thinking. (Examples: doing a chore, doing homework, talking about mad feelings, calming yourself down, being careful with toys, ignoring people who pick on you, etc.)

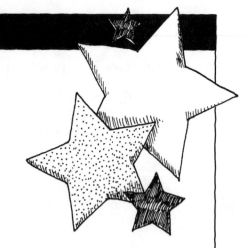

1. _____

2. _____

3. _____

4. _____

5. _____

In *Roadmaps* it is important to work on controlling your body in good ways all the time—not just with your sexual touching, but every day, in all parts of your life. Remember, you are learning to change your behavior and the way your brain works. You are learning about Right Body Control and Right Thinking!

Roadmaps is like driver's education, you are

learning how to control your body like a driver controls a car. Doing it the right way keeps you safe. Doing it the wrong way puts you and others in danger.

Buzzbee would go right off a cliff if he didn't use his brain and pay attention to where he was going.

Assignment 8E

Read each situation below and decide if the person is using Right Body Control or Wrong Body Control. Check the best answer for each situation.

1. Darryl runs around his group home and often bumps up against other kids.

   ❑ Right Body Control   ❑ Wrong Body Control

2. Donnie lives in a group home. One day he starts talking about a girl's bottom and makes fun of it by making hand gestures.

   ❑ Right Body Control   ❑ Wrong Body Control

3. Monica lives in a foster home. During her counseling session, she sits in her chair and talks about her life and her feelings.

   ❑ Right Body Control   ❑ Wrong Body Control

Assignment 8E (continued)

4. Doug doesn't know if he is ever going to move back home. One day he is told that he can't go home, so he runs away at night.

❑ Right Body Control   ❑ Wrong Body Control

5. Elizabeth lives in a foster home. Sometimes she turns talk sexual by making jokes about sex.

❑ Right Body Control   ❑ Wrong Body Control

6. Mark is happy when people come to visit him. When he notices that they have arrived, he walks up to them and smiles and offers his hand for a handshake. Sometimes he offers a hug if the visitors are family members.

❑ Right Body Control   ❑ Wrong Body Control

Good job! Using Right Body Control is something that you will need to practice every day from now on.

You are growing older, learning positive behaviors, and getting ready for a healthy life. I'm proud of you!

Learning to Control Your Body and Stay Out of Kids' Jail
(open book)

Name:_____

Date:_____

16 points possible. 14 points needed for passing.

Total Score:___/16   ❑ Pass   ❑ Need more work

1. List 3 good reasons to stay out of kids' jail or juvie. (3 points)

1)_____

2)_____

3)_____

2. Something that is illegal is: (1 point)

      A. ____OK to do.

      B. ____a good idea.

      C. ____against the law

      D. ____always the right way to do something.

For questions 3 and 4, decide if each situation is legal or illegal (against the law).

3. Alex likes a younger girl in the neighborhood. She is in 3rd grade, and Alex is in 7th grade. They end up touching each other's private parts. (1 point)

    ❑ Legal   ❑ Illegal (Against the Law)

4. John is 11 years old. He gives his 6-year-old sister $10 for letting him touch her private area. (1 point)

    ❑ Legal   ❑ Illegal (Against the Law)

5. List 3 times that you controlled your body in healthy ways this week. (3 points)

1) _____

2) _____

3) _____

6. Check all the things on this list that are illegal (against the law). (6 points)

    ❑ Your baby-sitter asks to touch your private parts.

    ❑ Your counselor pats you on the shoulder.

    ❑ The girl you like wants to give you a kiss after school.

❑ Your brother put his hand down your pants without asking.

❑ Your brother put his hand down your pants but asks first.

❑ Your friend shows you his privates when you are spending the night at his house, after you say you don't want to see them.

❑ Your best friend's big sister hugs you.

❑ A kid at school shows his privates in the bathroom at school.

❑ You break up with someone 2 hours after you ask them out.

❑ You touch a little girl's private parts without asking.

7. In *Roadmaps* it is important to work on controlling your body in good ways all the time, not just with sexual touching. (1 point)

❑ True   ❑ False

Fill in your progress chart for this chapter and get a sticker or a high-five from your counselor.

I control my speed, so I hope you will control your behavior too. You are cruising now! Keep following me!

HAPPY HEALTHY LIVING AHEAD

SAFETY 1

CHAPTER 9

Understanding the 4 Wrong Turns to Wrong Touching

No boy or girl is born wanting to do Wrong Touching. Almost every single child that does Wrong Touching has had stuff happen in their lives that led them to Wrong Thinking and wrong behavior. It's like wanting to go to a fun and wonderful place but being handed a Bad Map and taking wrong turn after wrong turn and ending up down the wrong road, at a dead end, or even running off a cliff! It is important to understand that Bad Maps were given to you by adults who were taking care of you. Those adults most likely had problems of their own, and they were not able to guide you to a healthy life.

How did you start down the wrong road, you might be wondering? And how can you keep yourself on the right road to healthy relationships and a good life?

In this chapter, we're taking a look at your Bad Map and how and where you got it. We are also looking at the wrong turns that keep you from going where you want to go. In chapter 14, "Learning to Be a Survivor," you'll learn how to ditch your Bad Map and start using a brand-new good one. You'll learn how to overcome your past bad experiences and leave them in the dust on the road behind you. In

Roadmaps we call this learning to be a Survivor, and chapter 14 will teach you how to get there.

One more thing you should know before starting in on this chapter. This is a hard chapter, because it asks you to think about things in your past that maybe you would rather not think about. Sometimes when bad things happen to us, we put those bad memories away and try not to think about them. In this chapter, you will be asked to try to remember some good things from your past and some bad things from your past. Since this is a hard chapter, we have built in some breaks that you and your counselor can take whenever you get too tired, frustrated, bored, or upset. Take those breaks if you need them, and then come back to *Roadmaps* when you feel fresh and ready.

Most kids take four wrong turns to run off the road and do Wrong Touching. These wrong turns are both things that happened to you and things that you did.

The Four Wrong Turns to Wrong Touching:

Wrong Turn #1: Getting a Bad Map and getting blocked by bad relationships that hurt you and didn't meet your needs

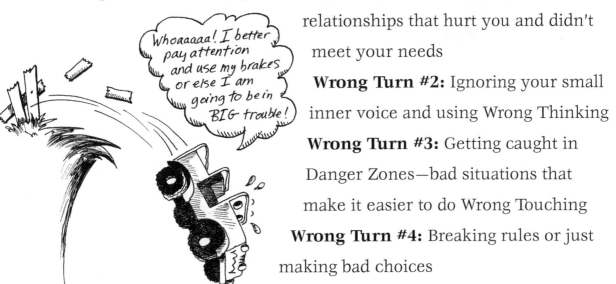

Wrong Turn #2: Ignoring your small inner voice and using Wrong Thinking

Wrong Turn #3: Getting caught in Danger Zones—bad situations that make it easier to do Wrong Touching

Wrong Turn #4: Breaking rules or just making bad choices

Buzzbee's friend Rita took these four wrong turns, and she's going to help you understand how it can happen. Rita is now 10 years old. She was sexually abused by her mom and dad and older brother, and then she did Wrong Sexual Touching with younger boys in her first foster home. Now she's living in her second foster home. Like you, Rita wants to understand how to stay on the road to building a healthy, happy life.

Wrong Turn #1: Getting a Bad Map and getting blocked by bad relationships that hurt you and didn't meet your needs

The first wrong turn to Wrong Touching was getting a Bad Map and getting blocked by bad relationships that hurt you and didn't meet your needs. That's because for most kids, Bad Maps come from their parents or other people who cared for them when they were young. Bad Maps come from things that happened in the past. Bad Maps are bad things that you were taught when you were young, and Bad

Maps mean that you did not learn some of the healthy things you should have learned. If your family is kind and loving, you are being given a Good Map. If your family is hurtful and harms you physically, sexually, or emotionally, or for whatever reason just can't meet your needs,

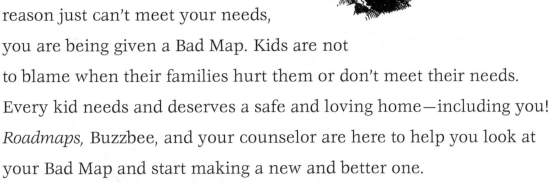

you are being given a Bad Map. Kids are not to blame when their families hurt them or don't meet their needs. Every kid needs and deserves a safe and loving home—including you! *Roadmaps,* Buzzbee, and your counselor are here to help you look at your Bad Map and start making a new and better one.

Like all kids everywhere, you needed and still need healthy, caring relationships to keep you safe and happy and to help you learn good ways to feel and to act. Healthy, caring relationships are important parts of a Good Map for staying on the right road to a healthy life and happy adventures. Healthy, caring relationships are ways that you get along with others so that you feel loved and smart and good, without hurting other people. In healthy, caring

relationships, you feel loving and friendly. You are kind to other people, and other people are kind to you.

For all kids, one of the most important things about healthy, caring relationships is that your *body and emotional needs* are met.

Body needs have to do with staying alive. They include things like being safe and warm and fed. Body needs include things like food, water, clothes, a good place to sleep, medicine when you need it, dental care, and someone to help you take care of yourself. While sex

is an important and good part of life when you're an adult, it is not a real body need because you can live without sex. You can't live without a true body need. Other body needs include exercise, space to move around in, light, and fresh air. These things help us stay alive and feel strong and healthy and good.

Emotional needs have to do with feeling loved, needed, and wanted. Some research has shown that emotional needs are almost as important as body needs in staying alive and staying healthy.

Emotional needs also have to do with believing in yourself and feeling like you are a capable and worthwhile person. Things like compliments, hugs, and smiles help meet your emotional needs. So do getting good grades or being good at drawing or baseball or music or anything at all that you care about. Sex is not a true emotional need, but sex can be a very good thing when your emotional needs

are being met, and you are an adult. When people talk to you, listen to you, spend time with you, share things with you, and say a true "I love you," you feel like a loved and worthwhile person. When people recognize your good behavior, however large or small, you feel like a loved and worthwhile person.

But when your body and emotional needs aren't met, when they are blocked, it is hard to have normal, healthy relationships. When your body and emotional needs are blocked, it's like you're driving down the road trying hard to get where you want to go and all of a sudden a big rock falls on the road and you can't go forward. This is called a *Roadblock*. Roadblocks are things that affect you now. For example, Rita's parents didn't take care of her, and they sexually abused her. In that way, they gave her a Bad Map when she was young, because they taught her that it was OK to do sexual things with children. Rita has found that she has several Roadblocks that came from her Bad Map. One, she doesn't trust adults, and two, she thinks about sexual touching all the time. These Roadblocks are causing her lots of problems right now. Roadblocks are not easy to get around. You might try to move the rock, you might try to turn around, you might look for a different road, but you can't get through! Roadblocks keep you from getting where you need to go. Roadblocks also may lead you to take the wrong road, like going down a dead end.

When you experience Roadblocks, and your body and emotional needs are **not** met, you may find yourself trying to get your needs met in unhealthy or wrong ways. You might feel an urge to do Wrong Sexual Touching and hurt someone.

Go ahead and take a break here. It will help if you move around, take a walk, or get a glass of water. When you and your counselor are ready, come back and start up right here.

Welcome back! Now let's look at your needs and at Rita's needs together we'll try to figure out how you got a Bad Map that sent you down the wrong road and how your road to healthy, caring relationships got blocked.

Understanding the Roadblocks to getting your needs met is very important. In the following assignment, you will explore your childhood experiences and find out where your past Bad Map and your present Roadblocks came from. This might be a hard assignment because it might bring up bad feelings. But it's an important assignment for helping you get back on the right road. Your counselor will support you as you work through your answers.

First, Rita will help you by sharing her answers to Assignment 9A, using her first home with her mom and dad.

Assignment 9A – Rita's Answers, Home 1

Family/Home 1: List who took care of you or the name of the home. Sometimes you might just say something like "The green house with the big yard."

Biological mom, dad, and older brother Mick.

How old were you when you lived in this home? (You can list from age ____ to age ____ or you can write how old you were and how long you lived there.)

I lived there from when I was born until I was 7 years old.

List the ways your body needs and emotional needs were met in that home (list of good things you remember about that home).

When Mom wasn't using drugs, she liked to braid my hair.

My mom made really good food when she wanted to. I liked her tuna casserole with potato chips.

My dad got me new tennis shoes and a new dress before he lost his job.

Mick tried to be a sort of dad to Rochelle and me; he liked to make hot dogs.

My mom told me that she loved me, when she wasn't using drugs.

My dad told me that I was beautiful.

My brother Mick told me that it was fun to play with me.

My mom told me I was very smart.

Great job!

Assignment 9A–Rita's Answers, Home 1 (continued)

Now list the ways your body needs and emotional needs were **not** met (list of things that were harmful or wrong in that home—the Bad Map).

We were always moving around.

We never had enough food to eat.

The power got turned off because there wasn't any money.

All the time Mom and Dad were using drugs and couldn't look after us so we tried to do it ourselves.

My dad and mom did sexual stuff to me.

My brother Mick touched my private parts and I ended up in the hospital.

My mom and dad would argue a lot, and they would yell bad things at each other.

There were lots of strange people in our house, and I felt scared a lot.

My parents often ignored me, and they never paid attention to me. It was like I didn't matter.

My parents taught me too much about sex. They showed me lots of movies showing people having sex.

No one ever took us to the doctor.

I always felt that the problems at home were my fault, because my parents complained about me a lot.

Assignment 9A–Rita's Answers, Home 1 (continued)

I was always changing schools and never felt like I fit in.

I didn't know how to brush my teeth so other kids called me stinky mouth and some of my teeth went bad.

My clothes always looked ratty and in winter my coat was too beat up to keep me warm.

My mom called me stupid and said I caused her too much stress.

Nobody did the laundry and I tried but the machine scared me and I didn't have money for the laundry soap.

When we lost our last apartment, we had to sleep in our car and then it got so bad we had to live in the homeless shelter.

One day some people came and beat up my mom and dad.

Wow, Rita sure had a mixed-up life. She went through some very hard times. Maybe you have gone through some very hard times too!

Now it's your turn to write about your life. Remembering some of these things might bring up bad feelings, but sharing good and bad experiences usually helps people get support, and it is one of the first steps to getting rid of your Bad Map and overcoming your Roadblocks to start a Good Map! If you have lived in lots of different homes, have your counselor help you pick out the most important homes you have lived in for this assignment.

Assignment 9A–Home 1

Family/Home 1: List who took care of you or the name of the home. Sometimes you might just say something like "The green house with the big yard."

_____

How old were you when you lived in this home? (You can list from age ____ to age ____ or you can write how old you were and how long you lived there.)

_____

List the ways your body needs and emotional needs were met in that home (list of good things you remember about that home).

_____

_____

_____

_____

_____

_____

_____

Assignment 9A–Home 1 (continued)

Now list the ways your body needs and emotional needs were **not** met (list of things that were harmful or wrong in that home—the Bad Map).

_____

_____

_____

_____

_____

_____

_____

Great job!

Assignment 9A–Home 2

Family/Home 2: List who took care of you or the name of the home. Sometimes you might just say something like "The apartment with the red carpet with Mr. and Mrs. Smith."

_____

How old were you when you lived in this home? (You can list from age ____ to age ____ or you can write how old you were and how long you lived there.)

_____

List the ways your body needs and emotional needs were met (list of good things you remember about that home).

_____

_____

_____

_____

_____

_____

_____

Assignment 9A–Home 2 (continued)

Now list the ways your body needs and emotional needs were **not** met (list of things that were harmful or wrong in that home—the Bad Map).

_____

_____

_____

_____

_____

_____

_____

_____

Great job! If you have lived in more than 2 homes, keep going. It is sometimes very hard to remember the past.

Great
job!

Assignment 9A–Home 3

Family/Home 3: List who took care of you or the name of the home. Sometimes you might just say something like "The tall house with the goat barn."

_____

How old were you when you lived in this home? (You can list from age ____ to age ____ or you can write how old you were and how long you lived there.)

_____

List the ways your body needs and emotional needs were met (list of good things you remember about that home).

_____

_____

_____

_____

_____

_____

_____

Assignment 9A–Home 3 (continued)

Now list the ways your body needs and emotional needs were **not** met (list of things that were harmful or wrong in that home—the Bad Map).

_____

_____

_____

_____

_____

_____

_____

_____

Nice remembering. If you lived in more than 3 homes, keep on going. Feel free to take a break whenever you get tired of remembering!

Assignment 9A–Home 4

Family/Home 4: List who took care of you or the name of the home.

_____

How old were you when you lived in this home? (You can list from age ____ to age ____ or you can write how old you were and how long you lived there.)

_____

List the ways your body needs and emotional needs were met (list of good things you remember about that home).

_____

_____

_____

_____

_____

_____

Assignment 9A–Home 4 (continued)

Now list the ways your body needs and emotional needs were **not** met (list of things that were harmful or wrong in that home—the Bad Map).

_____

_____

_____

_____

_____

_____

_____

_____

_____

Great job!

Great job answering these questions! It is sometimes very hard to remember the past.

If you have lived in more than 4 homes (and many, many children have), you will need more space and this assignment will take more time. Please ask your counselor for more copies of these pages, or use blank paper. Some kids have lived in as many as 15 or 20 different homes. No wonder it is hard to remember!

This was very hard work, and the things you remembered might bother you for a while. It is a good idea to talk to caring adults about those things you remember. It is very normal to keep remembering even more things after you finish this assignment. It is OK to ask your counselor to go back and add to the lists of good things and bad things you listed above.

For now, take a break to do something fun! When you come back to *Roadmaps,* you will learn more about the other wrong turns, and more about how to overcome your Bad Map and all your Roadblocks. Stop here until your next counseling session, or until your counselor and you decide to keep going.

Welcome back. Did you remember anything more about the places you lived when you were younger? If you did, go back and ask your counselor to help you add them to your lists from before.

Now, let's learn about the second wrong turn.

Whoaaaaa! I better pay attention and use my brakes or else I am going to be in BIG trouble!

Wrong Turn #2: Ignoring your small inner voice and using Wrong Thinking

We all have a small inner voice that tells us about right and wrong. This voice reminds us about what's a good way to treat others and what's harmful and hurtful. This little voice keeps us from making bad choices and doing things that hurt ourselves or other people.

Usually, when you want to do something you know is wrong, a little voice inside says, "Don't do it!" "Someone will see—you'll get in trouble!" "It's bad!" "It's wrong!" "It'll hurt the other person!" "You wouldn't like it if somebody did it to you!" Sometimes, though, when you have been given a Bad Map, you don't hear that voice, because you haven't learned those things. That little inner voice is really the same self-talk you learned about in chapter 5, "Right Thinking and Wrong Thinking."

Sometimes we listen to our small inner voice and stay on the right road to happy times together. This is called making good choices. But sometimes we use Wrong Thinking, also called Thinking Errors, to help us ignore that inner voice. We also learned about Thinking Errors in chapter 5.

Thinking Errors are lies that we tell ourselves so that we ignore the things that our little voice is trying to tell us. We use Thinking Errors to help us pretend for a while that our little voice isn't telling us the truth. When we use Thinking Errors, we run off the road and hurt other people. When we use Thinking Errors, we make bad choices.

Let's look at how you and Rita ignored that inner voice and used Wrong Thinking. First, Rita will help you by sharing her answers.

Assignment 9B—Rita's Answers

Think about a time that you did Wrong Sexual Behavior. Write down what kind of Wrong Touching you did that time.

I touched the two younger boys in the foster home on their privates.

What did your small inner voice tell you when you did the Wrong Touching?

1. This is bad.

2. They might tell.

3. I might get in trouble.

Now it's your turn.

Assignment 9B

Think about a time when you did Wrong Sexual Behavior. Write down what kind of Wrong Touching you did that time.

_____

What did your small inner voice tell you when you did the Wrong Touching?

1. _____

2. _____

3. _____

Good job! You were brave to be honest!

Take another break. This is a long chapter, and it is good to rest and refuel before continuing. When your counselor says it is OK to continue, you will learn about Danger Zones, which are places to avoid so that you will stay out of trouble.

Welcome back. Now you will learn about the third wrong turn: Danger Zones.

Whoaaaaa! I better pay attention and use my brakes or else I am going to be in BIG trouble!

Wrong Turn #3: Getting caught in Danger Zones—bad situations that make it easier to do Wrong Touching

For kids a Danger Zone usually means a bad living situation. Kids can't usually change their living situations because grownups are supposed to keep kids safe. It is not your fault that adults made bad choices when you were younger. But every kid can learn to spot danger. Were there things in your home that made you want to do Wrong Touching? Were there things in your home that made it easier to do Wrong Touching? Did the grownups watch porno movies when you were around or do sexual stuff in front of you? Did younger and older kids sleep together in the same room or in the same bed? Were you often left without good supervision? These are common things that add up to Danger Zones.

Remember, it is not your fault that you lived in Danger Zones when you were younger, but it is your job to learn to avoid Danger Zones in the future.

Here are some other possible Danger Zones that you might have experienced:

You saw people having sex, so you wanted to have sex.

You used the Internet a lot, and you saw lots of sexy
pictures that gave you ideas.

Other people did sexual touching to you, and that
gave you the idea.

You slept in the same room with your brother or sister.

People were always fighting and using drugs, and nobody
paid attention to you.

You and your family really didn't have enough food.
You just stole whatever you wanted.

People were always hurting each other.

Nobody ever taught you about how to act.

Now let's look at your Danger Zones for Wrong Touching. First Rita will help you by sharing her answers. She's chosen to write about her first foster home, where she started doing Wrong Touching.

Assignment 9C—Rita's Answers

Write down a living situation where you were caught in lots of Danger Zones. You might want to pick the home where you started having touching problems or the home where you had the most touching problems. Your counselor can help you choose.

My first foster home with the 2 boys, where I started doing Wrong Touching

Now write down what you remember about some of the things in this living situation that made it easier for you to do Wrong Touching.

1. *I wasn't being watched.*

2. *I watched the sexy movies.*

3. *I slept in the same room with the little boys.*

Now it's your turn.

Assignment 9C

Write down a living situation where you were caught in lots of Danger Zones. You might want to pick the home where you started having touching problems or the home where you had the most touching problems. Your counselor can help you choose.

_____

Now write down what you remember about some of the things in this living situation that made it easier for you to do Wrong Touching.

1. _____

2. _____

3. _____

4. _____

Great job! In the next chapter, you will make a list of Special Safety Rules to play it safe! Making sure you are not alone with younger kids will help.

You are getting through this chapter in good time. If you or your counselor would like a break, take one here. When you come back, you will learn about the fourth wrong turn, breaking rules and making bad choices.

Welcome back! If you are ready, it's time to learn about the fourth wrong turn.

Whoaaaaa! I better pay attention and use my brakes or else I am going to be in BIG trouble!

Wrong Turn #4: Breaking rules or just making bad choices

First, you got a Bad Map and ran into Roadblocks that kept you from getting your needs met. Then you took a wrong turn to find other ways to meet your needs. Second, you used Thinking Errors to take a wrong turn and ignore your small inner voice. Third, you got caught in Danger Zones that made it easier to do Wrong Touching. The last wrong turn was breaking rules or just making bad choices.

After being given a Bad Map, running into Roadblocks, ignoring your inner voice, and using Thinking Errors, and after running into Danger Zones, it is easy to understand why many kids develop problem behaviors. In this section, you will look at the choices you made that played a part in starting your touching problems. By learning about how you broke rules and made bad choices, you will learn how to change your behavior so that you can always stay on the right road.

Remember, by understanding your bad choices, you will be learning how to make new, good choices that will lead to a healthy life.

HAPPY HEALTHY LIVING AHEAD

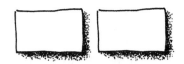

In Assignment 9D, you'll be asked to think about some of the Wrong Sexual Behavior that you did in the past. How did you get away with your Wrong Sexual Behavior? What rules did you break in order to do the Wrong Behavior? First Rita will help you by sharing her answers.

Assignment 9D—Rita's Answers

Write down some of the ways you broke rules or made bad choices in order to do Wrong Touching.

1. I was sneaky, and I would go where the adults couldn't see me.

2. I shut the door to my bedroom so nobody would see what I was doing.

3. I lied and told my foster mother that I was only playing house.

4. I gave one of my foster brothers my allowance and one my dessert for a week so he'd let me touch him .

Now it's your turn.

Assignment 9D

Write down some of the ways you broke rules or made bad choices in order to do Wrong Touching.

1. _____

2. _____

3. _____

4. _____

When you take any of the four wrong turns, you can end up going down wrong roads and dead ends, running into lots of Roadblocks, or even driving off a cliff! That's why in *Roadmaps* you are learning to avoid the 4 wrong turns and instead choose the 4 right ways to keep yourself on the road to a happy and healthy life.

The 4 Right Ways to a Happy and Healthy Life:

1. Learn to build healthy relationships that meet your needs. Watch out for Roadblocks!

2. Listen to your small inner voice that tells you about right and wrong and learn to use Right Thinking.

3. Play it safe! Keep away from Danger Zones that make it easier to do Wrong Touching.

4. Follow your Special Safety Rules, and make good choices like respecting boundaries. You can learn about Special Safety Rules in chapter 10, "Keeping Yourself and Others Safe with Special Safety Rules and Good Boundaries."

These 4 right ways are like guardrails on a twisty highway. They keep you from going off track and hurting yourself or other people. By following these 4 rules, you will care about other people, you will care about whether your actions are helping them or hurting them, and you will treat other kids and adults the way you want them to treat you. The more you learn to drive these roads, the more happy times and good adventures you will have. These good choices will lead you to a happy and healthy life.

Great job! You are learning to ditch your Bad Map and overcome your Roadblocks, use Right Thinking, follow good Safety Rules, and make good choices that respect other people.

Understanding the
4 Wrong Turns to Wrong Touching
(open book)

Name:_____

Date:_____

17 points possible. 16 points needed for passing.

Total Score:___/17   ❏ Pass   ❏ Need more work

1. Boys and girls are born wanting to do Wrong Touching. (1 point)
    ❏ True   ❏ False

2. By overcoming their past bad experiences, people will become: (1 point)

    A.___ victims.

    B. ___criminals.

    C.___ unhappy and sad.

    D.___ Survivors.

3. Bad Maps come from: (1 point)

    A. ___ bad stores.

    B. ___ bad life experiences.

    C. ___ bad computers.

    D. ___ bad newspapers.

4. Healthy, caring relationships are important parts of a Good Map for staying on the right road to a happy and healthy life. (1 point)

     ❑ True   ❑ False

5. Roadblocks: (1 point)

     A. ___ are only found on mountain passes.

     B. ___ help you stay on the right road.

     C. ___ sometimes lead to bad choices.

     D.___ are easy to break through.

6. Danger Zones: (1 point)

     A. ___ are always labeled with flashing yellow lights.

     B. ___ are usually found in bad living situations.

     C.___ can usually be ignored because they don't really matter.

     D.___ don't apply to smart people.

7. Thinking Errors are: (1 point)

     A. ___ lies we tell others.

     B. ___ lies we tell ourselves so that we ignore the things that our little voice is trying to tell us.

     C. ___ something that only smart people use.

     D. ___ problems that adults have because they are too old to think correctly.

8. Building healthy relationships helps people get along with others and helps keep them from hurting other people. (1 point)

    ❑ True   ❑ False

9. Check all the things on this list that are true body needs. (4 points)

    ❑ Food

    ❑ Water

    ❑ Sex

    ❑ Drawing

    ❑ Shelter

    ❑ Exercise

10. Check all the things on this list that are true emotional needs. (3 points)

    ❑ Compliments

    ❑ Sex

    ❑ Encouragement and rewards

    ❑ Positive activities that you are good at

    ❑ Money

11. Sex is a true body need. (1 point)

    ❑ True   ❑ False

12. Wrong Thinking is also called a Thinking Error. (1 point)

    ❑ True   ❑ False

Fill in your progress chart and get a sticker or a high-five from your counselor. You are making great progress now!

CHAPTER 10

Keeping Yourself and Others Safe with Special Safety Rules and Good Boundaries

Special Safety Rules help people stop Wrong Touching. Rules are like guardrails on a twisty highway. They keep you from going off track and hurting yourself or other people. Rules help young people stay away from kids' jail!

Rules are especially important if you live with younger children. If you live with younger children, you will need to make some Special Safety Rules to follow at all times.

Josie, age 7, has touching problems. Before she started treatment, Josie had touched both of her younger brothers in their private parts. With her counselor's help, Josie made some Special Safety Rules to help her **not** do Wrong Touching. These rules help keep Josie's younger brothers safe.

Here are Josie's Special Safety Rules to help her stop doing sexual touching:

Josie's Special Safety Rules for Staying Out of Trouble

1. Don't sneak up on my brothers.

2. Don't be alone with them at all, unless an adult is around and watching.

3. No punching, touching, or grabbing.

4. Do not wrestle with my brothers.

5. Do not go into my brothers' bedrooms for any reason.

6. Do not play house with my brothers.

7. Do not talk about sex with my brothers.

8. No going in the bathroom when anyone is in there.

9. Do not tickle my brothers.

10. Keep the bathroom door closed when I am using it.

I agree to always follow these rules.

Josie L.   July 1, 2007

Assignment 10A

Now make up your own list of Special Safety Rules that will help you avoid Wrong Touching.

1. _____

2. _____

3. _____

4. _____

5. _____

6. _____

7. _____

8. _____

Assignment 10B

Now ask your counselor, parents, foster parents, or group home staff for other ideas about your Special Safety Rules. Talk to at least 2 different adults. Show them your list of Special Safety Rules from Assignment 10A. Then write down their comments about your list, and then write down any more rules they can think of. After you talk with each adult, thank them for helping you!

Assignment 10B (continued)

Adult #1: Name:_____

What does this person think about your list of Special Safety Rules?
What are their comments?

_____

_____

_____

What other Special Safety Rules can this person think of?

_____

_____

_____

Adult #2: Name:_____

What does this person think about your list of Special Safety Rules?
What are their comments?

_____

_____

_____

Assignment 10B (continued)

What other Special Safety Rules can this person think of?

_____

_____

_____

_____

SAFETY
1

Rules help keep us safe. Rules help keep us on the right road for happy adventures.

Assignment 10C

Now use the form on the next page to make a complete list of your Special Safety Rules. These rules will keep you and others safe, but you will need to follow them at all times. After you and your counselor have made the list, make sure you both sign it. Then ask other important adults in your life to sign too. This list will become one of the most important parts of the Safety Plan Book that you will make later on in chapter 16!

My Special Safety Rules

Name:_____ Date:_____

These are the Special Safety Rules that I have made to help keep myself and others safe. I agree to follow all of these rules, and everyone else who signs this page agrees to help me follow these rules.

1. _____

2. _____

3. _____

4. _____

5. _____

6. _____

7. _____

8. _____

I agree to always follow these rules:

_____Date:_____

We agree to support _____ in always following these rules:

_____ Date:_____   _____ Date:_____

_____ Date:_____   _____ Date:_____

_____ Date:_____   _____ Date:_____

_____ Date:_____   _____ Date:_____

Your Special Safety Rules are important for preventing Wrong Touching, and rules about boundaries are important for making friends and getting along with other people. There are many kinds of boundaries, and in *Roadmaps* you will learn how to pay attention to boundaries and to respect boundaries no matter where you are or who you are with.

Boundaries are like fences people put around things that they want to keep private—just for themselves—or that they want treated a certain way. You can put boundaries around things or places, like your iPod or CD player, your clothes, this workbook, or your room. You can put boundaries around your own body, around how other people can touch you, or around how close they can be to you. You can also put boundaries around your feelings or your past experiences. Sometimes

people don't like to talk about their father, their mother, or their childhood because it makes them feel bad. They have a boundary around talking about their families.

Boundaries say, "This is mine—please respect that." That is why your friends can't just walk off with your toys or music, and that is why people who steal go to jail. Boundaries help us feel safe with others.

Here are some of Bettina's boundaries:

1. I don't like people touching my face.

2. I don't like people using my clothes.

3. I don't like people getting too close to me—it makes me nervous.

4. I don't like people talking to me about my mother.

We all have a right to tell other people what our boundaries are, especially when they have to do with keeping our bodies and our feelings safe.

Assignment 10D

In the space below, write down some of your boundaries. Be creative. You can list any and all boundaries you can think of.

1. _____

2. _____

3. _____

4. _____

5. _____

Some kinds of boundaries are more like rules about how to behave with other people. Remember when you learned not to pick your nose in front of others? That is a social behavior rule, or boundary. Have you ever gone into someone's house and they asked you to take off your shoes? That is a common household rule, and it is also a boundary. People make that rule so that their carpets and floors stay cleaner.

Sometimes boundary rules can be tricky because they are mostly unspoken. People expect you to just know them and to behave in a certain way without being told. But what if nobody ever taught you?

Bryan, age 11, didn't understand boundaries when he started treatment for his sexual behavior problems. He didn't know how to talk to people or be with them in a nice way. He would do things like cover his face when he talked or flip his legs up so that his bottom was showing. Now Bryan has learned some rules about boundaries that help him get along better in his foster home and at school.

I have to always ask before touching a person. Before I started counseling, I would just walk up to a person and put my arms around them. Sometimes I would sit or stand so that I was touching the other person. Now I know about personal space. We also call it boundaries. A boundary is like a personal bubble

around a person. Now I have a 2-foot rule. With my rule I try to stay 2 feet away from other people unless I have permission to get closer.

Understanding boundaries has helped Bryan stay out of trouble. What's more, he is feeling very happy that he's getting along better with other kids and with adults.

Boundaries help people live together in families, friendships, and groups of all sorts like schools, teams, and neighborhoods. Healthy people try very hard to respect other people's boundaries.

Assignment 10E

Now ask your counselor what the boundaries are in their office. Find out what things you can touch, and what things you should leave alone. Write down the things you should leave alone in the space below.

1. _____

2. _____

3. _____

4. _____

5. _____

6. _____

Assignment 10F

Sometime during the next week, ask an adult you trust—like your mom or dad, one of your foster parents, or a staff member at your group home—what their boundaries are at home. You might have to explain what a boundary is. Write down what the person says in the space below.

What is the name of the person you talked with?

_____

What are their boundaries at home?

1. _____

2. _____

3. _____

4. _____

5. _____

Assignment 10G

Daily Boundary Practice Form

Practice paying attention to boundaries every day. Your counselor will help you decide how long you should do this assignment. Practice makes perfect!

Date: _____

Write down 1 thing you did today where you respected the boundaries of another person.

_____

_____

_____

Write down 1 thing you did today where you did not do a very good job of respecting someone's boundaries.

_____

_____

_____

Making and following Special Safety Rules is an important part of your treatment. In this chapter, you have made a list of your own rules that will keep you and others safe. Now it is up to you to follow those rules and make them work!

In addition to your Special Safety Rules, in this chapter you have learned about boundaries. We all have boundaries—around our things; around our homes, rooms, or offices; around our bodies; and around our feelings. We all have a right to tell other people what our boundaries are, and we all have a responsibility to respect other people's boundaries.

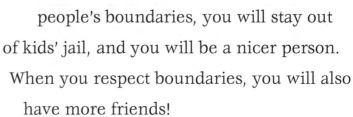

Respecting boundaries means staying away from whatever is inside the boundary and whatever bothers other people.

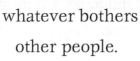

Leave my engine alone—that's my boundary!

By respecting people's boundaries, you will stay out of kids' jail, and you will be a nicer person. When you respect boundaries, you will also have more friends!

ROAD TEST 10

Keeping Yourself and Others Safe with Special Safety Rules and Good Boundaries
(open book)

Name:_____

Date:_____

15 points possible. 13 points needed for passing.

Total Score:___/15   ❑ Pass   ❑ Need more work

1. What is a boundary? (2 points)

_____

_____

_____

2. List 3 of your Special Safety Rules that help you avoid Wrong Touching. (3 points)

1) _____

2) _____

3) _____

3. Why is it important to respect other people's boundaries? (2 points)

_____

_____

_____

_____

_____

4. List 3 boundaries in your home, foster home, or group home. (3 points)

1) _____

2) _____

3) _____

5. List 3 boundaries in your counselor's office. (3 points)

1) _____

2) _____

3) _____

6. List 2 of your boundaries (things that you do not like other people touching or talking about). (2 points)

1) _____

2) _____

Fill in your progress chart for this chapter and get a sticker or a high-five from your counselor.

You are moving at just the right speed!

HAPPY HEALTHY LIVING AHEAD

SAFETY 1

CHAPTER 11

Talking About Touching That People Have Done to You

In *Roadmaps* you are learning to control your Wrong Sexual Touching. One way to do this is to try to think back to where you learned about Wrong Sexual Touching. Once you figure out where you learned about Wrong Sexual Touching, it will be much easier to stop!

Because you are young, learning to stop doing something can be easier than it is for adults. You are always learning, and it is never too late to learn new things.

Take a few moments to read this letter that Betty wrote to her friends in her counseling group. The letter was written by Betty when it was her turn to tell the others about her past bad experiences. As you can tell, writing or talking about a past or recent bad experience can be very hard. Betty was very brave when she wrote this letter.

Dear Friends,

I wanted to write to you to tell you about something that happened to me. When I was 4 years old, my stepdad began touching me in my privates. He also made me rub his penis and suck on it. At first, I really liked it and it felt really good to have him touch me like that, because I knew that my dad loved me and that was how he showed it. He always gave me special attention and sometimes he got me special

treats. I don't want him to stop loving me because I'm telling on him. He told me that it was our secret and that I would always be special to him.

I'm 9 now, and I know that it's my fault that this has gone on this long. I never wanted to tell anyone because I didn't want my dad to stop loving me. I'm sure there must be something I could have done to stop it. I have been thinking about a lot of stuff, like that my mom is going to be so mad at me when she finds out, and that nobody is going to believe me. What if I get in trouble for letting this happen to me? Should I tell anyone, and if so, who?

What if I tell an adult and they don't believe me? Sometimes I wonder if my mom knows because she hasn't done anything to stop it. Maybe she is mad at me and doesn't love me anymore. I'm really embarrassed to tell anyone because I know people will make fun of me. Nobody is going to understand this, and I'm sure that nobody I know has had to go through this. I feel ashamed and dirty because sometimes I liked it and wanted the attention.

I don't want to get my dad in trouble either, and I'm really scared that he is not going to love me anymore if I tell on him. What should I do?

Sincerely,

Betty

After writing the letter to her friends in her counseling group, called a *Survivor's Group,* Betty received the following letter back from one of her friends in the group. The letter helped Betty understand that she was not alone, and it helped her move from being a victim to being a Survivor. You will hear more about victims and survivors in chapter 14, "Learning to Be a Survivor."

Dear Betty,

Thank you for trusting me and telling me what was happening to you. Are you OK? I believe you and it is not your fault.

I think that you need to tell an adult what happened. Maybe you should tell your counselor. You could tell your grandparents or maybe somebody else from your family. I know it may be scary, but you could tell your mom. She will believe you and be mad at your dad for what he did to you. Be serious and honest with your mom and you won't be in trouble. If your mom does not believe you, you can tell the police. Tell until someone believes you.

This is not your fault. Your dad is an adult and he is responsible. It is not right for adults to do sexual things with kids. I think your dad needs counseling and help for his touching problems. Tell your dad how you feel. Tell him that you do not like it when he does those things.

If your dad is still in your home and you feel unsafe, maybe you could go live with another family member. Or, you can come to my house where it is safe after school. You should make sure that you are never alone with your dad.

I am sorry that this happened to you. It happened to me too and you are not alone. I am your friend and I will not laugh at you. I will support you and help you.

I hope everything turns out OK.

Sincerely,

Your friend Gina

Betty was very glad that she had a friend who could understand what happened to her. In *Roadmaps* you have Buzzbee, who has been your guide. You also have your counselor, who has been supporting you in your work in *Roadmaps*. You may also have other people you can trust, like a parent, foster parent, caseworker, or group home staff. For now,

what you are going to write in *Roadmaps* will be just
between you, Buzzbee, and your counselor.
If you want, you might choose to
share what you write
with someone else on
your treatment team.
This is a big step in
your treatment, and
you should be proud
that you are brave
enough to work on this chapter
in *Roadmaps*.

Sometimes it can seem sad or scary, but it really helps to get your feelings and memories out!

Assignment 11A

Think about where you first learned about sexual touching.
Remember what you saw in person or on TV, or what happened to
you. Think about your past and answer the questions. Put "none"
in the blanks if you've never had that experience.

1. How did you first learn about sex?

_____

2. How many other people have you ever seen having sex or doing
   sexual things to each other? (List their names.)

_____

Assignment 11A (continued)

3. List all the people who have ever taught or shown you anything about sex.

_____

4. Explain how many pictures you have seen where people are naked, or are having sex. Say if you saw the pictures in magazines, in movies, on TV, or on the Internet.

_____

5. Who was the first person who ever touched you in a sexual way?

_____

6. How old were you when it happened? _____ years old

7. How old was the other person? _____ years old

8. What did that person do?

_____

9. Where were you living when it happened?

_____

Assignment 11A (continued)

10. How did you feel when the other person did the sexual touching to you?

_____

_____

11. Who was the second person who ever touched you in a sexual way?

_____

12. How old were you when it happened? _____ years old

13. How old was the other person? _____ years old

14. What did that person do?

_____

15. Where were you living when it happened?

_____

16. How did you feel when the other person did the sexual touching to you?

_____

_____

Assignment 11A (continued)

17. Now list any other people who have ever touched you in your private parts or had you touch them in their private parts.

_____

_____

_____

_____

Assignment 11B

What is the earliest thing you can remember about your life? Think about when you were very young. Write down what you remember.

_____

_____

_____

_____

It will help you stop your Wrong Sexual Touching if you start talking about your feelings instead of keeping them inside.

Talking about your feelings with a good friend or an adult who cares about you is a very healthy thing and it can help clear out the Roadblocks from your life. Learning to talk about feelings is an important part of *Roadmaps.* You may want to talk about feelings you had when someone did Wrong Sexual Touching to you. Or you may want to talk about other feelings you have every day.

Here are some people you might want to try talking to about feelings:

> your mom or dad
>
> your counselor
>
> the grownups at the group home
>
> your foster parents
>
> a school counselor or a
>> teacher you like
>
> an aunt or uncle or
>> grandparents
>
> your best friend

You have got to talk about your feelings if you want to live a healthy life!

There are some people you might **not** want to talk to about your feelings:

> people who did Wrong Touching to you
>
> people who tell other people what you tell them without your
>> permission
>
> people who make fun of you for talking about feelings

Assignment 11C

Make a list of people you know you can talk to about your feelings.

1. _____

2. _____

3. _____

4. _____

If you were touched by someone who was older than you—whether an older kid, teenager, or grownup—you might have some feelings inside that you don't tell other people about. Boys and girls who have been sexually touched by older people have lots of different feelings. Here is a list of some:

scared	angry
bored	guilty
empty	sexy
confused	hurt
ashamed	lonely
helpless	

Sometimes it helps to draw a picture about what happened to you. Sometimes pictures work better than words.

Assignment 11D

In this space, draw a picture about another person touching you in a sexual way. Ask your counselor to help label each person in the picture. If you want, you can draw on a different piece of paper and cut out the picture and paste it or staple it on this page. If nobody has touched you in a sexual way, draw a picture of another person hurting you in some other way.

No doubt about it, this chapter is hard work. Remembering things from your past can sometimes bring up angry feelings, sad feelings, or even sexual feelings. Remember, one of the best ways to handle feelings is to talk about them with another person, like someone on your treatment team. Exercise might also help calm you down. Sometimes just taking a nap makes people feel better. Later in *Roadmaps,* you will do some work with the information you just shared. You will learn how to grow from being the victim of a bad childhood experience to being a Survivor. *Roadmaps* will show you how to get past all the Roadblocks to become a Survivor.

ROAD TEST
11

Talking About Touching That People Have Done to You
(open book)

Name:_____

Date:_____

6 points possible. 5 points needed for passing.

Total Score:___/6   ❏ Pass   ❏ Need more work

1. It will help you stop your Wrong Touching if you start talking about your feelings instead of keeping them inside. (1 point)
   ❏ True   ❏ False

2. Boys and girls who have been sexually touched by older people have lots of different feelings (1 point)
   ❏ True   ❏ False

3. Who should you talk to about your feelings? (1 point)

   A. ____ The bully at school

   B. ____ Anyone, even if they tell others about it

   C. ____ People who are only mean to me some of the time

   D. ____ People who really care about me

4. It is easier for young people to learn to stop doing something than it is for adults. (1 point)

❑ True   ❑ False

5. How much of the Wrong Touching that other people have done to you have you told someone about so far? (1 point)

A. ___ None of it

B. ___ Some of it

C. ___ Most of it

D. ___ All of it, totally

6. Remembering things from your past can bring up bad feelings. (1 point)

❑ True   ❑ False

Great job! Fill in your progress chart for this chapter and get a sticker or a high-five from your counselor.

Remembering things from your past can bring up bad feelings, but sharing those feelings can help you feel better. So keep on truckin'! No Roadblocks for you!

HAPPY HEALTHY LIVING AHEAD

SAFETY 1

CHAPTER 12

Telling the Truth About Your Wrong Touching

In this chapter, you will be asked to talk about your own touching problems. This might not be easy. Talking about Wrong Touching can be scary, embarrassing, or just plain hard. But you can do it, and it will help you get on the right road and stay out of kids' jail.

Remember back in chapter 5, "Right Thinking and Wrong Thinking," when you learned about denial? Many people have problems with denial. In *Roadmaps* you don't have to worry about people judging you or about getting into trouble. In *Roadmaps* we know that it takes a strong and brave person to talk about Wrong Touching problems.

It can be hard to admit your mistakes. It's hard to tell the truth about something you did that hurt someone else. It's hard to tell the truth about when you broke a rule. Sometimes people even lie and make up stories to keep from getting caught and getting in trouble. In *Roadmaps* it is important to keep on doing Right Thinking and not do Wrong Thinking. It's like following a good paved road and not taking any turns onto bumpy dirt roads that lead to dead ends or off a cliff.

Admitting your past mistakes keeps you on the right road. By doing this, you get rid of your denial and make real progress!

Rosa has something to share about telling the truth.

I was really scared when I told my counselor about all the touching I have done. But then it felt good to talk about it and learn that I was not alone.

Telling the truth about what you did is like taking your car to the mechanic. The mechanic can't fix what's wrong if you make up a different story and don't tell what's really happening. If the car is backfiring but you say the brakes are squealing, the backfiring problem probably isn't going to get fixed.

In *Roadmaps* you have to tell the truth about your past Wrong Touching so that you can make a good safety plan to keep from doing it again in the future. Your counselor, parents, or foster parents will help you use the information to make a Safety Plan Book, which we will explain in chapter 16.

Assignment 12A

You probably have some reasons and some feelings about why you don't want to tell the truth about your Wrong Touching. Write down 3 of them.

1. _____

2. _____

3. _____

Assignment 12B

Now write down 5 reasons for telling the whole truth about your touching problem.

1. _____

2. _____

3. _____

4. _____

5. _____

Next you will make a list of every person you have ever touched in a sexual way, and every Wrong Sexual Behavior problem that you have ever had. This helps you get rid of secrets.

Keeping secrets about sexual touching is not good. It's like a garbage can that's overflowing. Not only can it get stinky, but it also takes a lot of energy to keep the lid on those secrets. It is time to open up that garbage can and let those secrets out. It is time to tell the truth. Keeping secrets about Wrong Touching do esn't help you stop. Keeping those secrets is like a false road sign that will send you straight to kids' jail! It's time to take the lid off your can of secrets.

Assignment 12C

Check every sexual behavior you have ever done in the list below.

Be sure to check every box that in all honesty applies to you. Remember, you are not in trouble for these things now. Admitting to past problems will help you find a better road for the future!

❑ Talked about private parts in school or around other people

❑ Talked about sex or private parts online (on the computer or Internet)

❑ Looked at pictures of naked people or sex on the Internet

Assignment 12C (continued)

❑ Wrote notes about sex or private parts

❑ Drew pictures of people's private parts or people having sex

❑ Touched the private parts of an animal(s)

❑ Tried to have sex with an animal(s)

❑ Stared at a person's private parts too much

❑ Called people sexual names

❑ Made sexual gestures with your hands

❑ Took another person's underwear

❑ Asked another person to have sex with you

❑ Touched another person's private parts but pretended
   it was an accident

❑ Touched another person's private parts without asking

❑ Touched another person's private parts, like bottoms or breasts

❑ Walked around without any clothes on

❑ Showed your private parts to another person

❑ Touched your own private parts in front of other people

❑ Touched your own private parts so much they hurt

❑ Put things in your private parts

Assignment 12C (continued)

❑ Pretended to have sex by humping a stuffed animal
  or something else

❑ Had sex with another person

Great job! By being honest and admitting to your past behavior, you are taking a big step toward becoming a member of the Sexual Abuse Prevention and Safety Team!

Now, if you have ever touched another person's private parts, it is time to explain what you have done. If you have never touched another person's private parts, or haven't touched as many people as there are blanks, just write "no more" in the blank for the person's name. If you need extra blanks, ask your counselor for extra copies of the blanks.

Assignment 12D

In the spaces on the next pages, write the name of a person you touched and then answer the questions. If there are more spaces than people you have touched, just write "no more" in the extra spaces.

Assignment 12D (continued)

Person's name: _____

Person's age when you touched them: _____

Your age when you touched them: _____

Which private parts did you touch? (Circle what you touched.)

penis   bottom

vulva   vagina
(girl's outside private part)   *(girl's inside private part)*

breasts   mouth

What did you touch the person with? (Circle what you used to touch)

hand   finger

mouth   penis

breasts   object

How many times did you do sexual touching to this person?

_____

Where were you living when you did the touching to this person?

_____

Assignment 12D (continued)

Person's name: _____

Person's age when you touched them: _____

Your age when you touched them: _____

Which private parts did you touch? (Circle what you touched.)

penis	bottom
vulva	vagina
(girl's outside private part)	*(girl's inside private part)*
breasts	mouth

What did you touch the person with? (Circle what you used to touch)

hand	finger
mouth	penis
breasts	object

How many times did you do sexual touching to this person?

_____

Where were you living when you did the touching to this person?

_____

Assignment 12D (continued)

Person's name: _____

Person's age when you touched them: _____

Your age when you touched them: _____

Which private parts did you touch? (Circle what you touched.)

penis	bottom
vulva *(girl's outside private part)*	vagina *(girl's inside private part)*
breasts	mouth

What did you touch the person with? (Circle what you used to touch)

hand	finger
mouth	penis
breasts	object

How many times did you do sexual touching to this person?

_____

Where were you living when you did the touching to this person?

_____

Assignment 12D (continued)

Person's name: _____

Person's age when you touched them: _____

Your age when you touched them: _____

Which private parts did you touch? (Circle what you touched.)

penis   bottom

vulva   vagina

(girl's outside private part)   *(girl's inside private part)*

breasts   mouth

What did you touch the person with? (Circle what you used to touch)

hand   finger

mouth   penis

breasts   object

How many times did you do sexual touching to this person?

_____

Where were you living when you did the touching to this person?

_____

Assignment 12D (continued)

Person's name: _____

Person's age when you touched them: _____

Your age when you touched them: _____

Which private parts did you touch? (Circle what you touched.)

penis	bottom
vulva *(girl's outside private part)*	vagina *(girl's inside private part)*
breasts	mouth

What did you touch the person with? (Circle what you used to touch)

hand	finger
mouth	penis
breasts	object

How many times did you do sexual touching to this person?

_____

Where were you living when you did the touching to this person?

_____

Good job! Admitting and telling the whole truth about your sexual touching problems is a very big step in your treatment. If you have been honest with this assignment, then you can be very proud of yourself.

It takes courage to be honest! You are doing a great job. Keep on moving!

ROAD TEST 12

Telling the Truth
About Your Wrong Touching
(open book)

Name:_____

Date:_____

7 points possible. 6 points needed for passing.

Total Score:___/7   ❑ Pass   ❑ Need more work

1. Talking about Wrong Touching is always easy. (1 point)
    ❑ True   ❑ False

2. It takes a strong and brave person to talk about Wrong Touching problems. (1 point)

        ❏ True   ❏ False

3. What is 1 good reason someone would not want to talk about their Wrong Touching problem? (1 point)

1)_____

4. List 2 good reasons someone should tell the whole truth about their Wrong Touching problems. (2 points)

1)_____

2)_____

5. Keeping your Wrong Touching secret will help you stop doing it. (1 point)

        ❏ True   ❏ False

6. Admitting and telling the whole truth about your own sexual touching problems means: (1 point)

      A. ___ you are done with treatment.

      B. ___ you are a bad person.

      C. ___ you have taken a big step in treatment.

      D. ___ you will now get into trouble and go to jail.

Fill in your progress chart for this chapter and get a sticker or a high-five from your counselor.

CHAPTER 13

Understanding How You Have Hurt People and Apologizing for Your Wrong Touching

Now it is time to think about how your actions have hurt other people. You can't change your past behavior, but you can take a huge step toward joining the Sexual Abuse Prevention and Safety Team by apologizing for your past mistakes. Apologizing helps you feel better about your past problems, and it helps other people feel better about you too! Apologizing shows how much you've learned and changed. It shows that you accept responsibility for what you did and that you don't want to hurt anyone in that way ever again. This kind of letter is called a *clarification letter,* or *apology letter.*

Here is what Kaitlyn, age 9, wrote to her 6-year-old brother, Karl. She wrote the letter after she had been in counseling for about 4 months.

January 23

Dear Karl,

I am very sorry I hurt you in your private parts. I am getting help now. I will not do it again! I can remember touching and hurting you on the privates about 10 times with my hand. I also touched you and made you put your penis in my private parts 4 times. I can understand why you are sometimes scared to be around me. What I did to you was very wrong. I am working in counseling so I will not hurt you again.

I will not chase you at school, because I don't want you to feel scared. I am also going to follow all of my treatment rules from now on.

Your sister,
Kaitlyn

Your letter should cover these points:

1. Include today's date.

2. Include a greeting (like Dear or Hello) using the person's right name.

3. Give an apology (saying I'm sorry) for your Wrong Touching.

4. Write exactly what you did to the other person. Write how you touched him or her. Say how many times you did it.

5. Admit if you lied about it or blamed it on the other person.

6. Write that the touching was your fault and not the victim's fault.

7. Say what you are doing to stop your Wrong Touching.

8. Give another apology for your Wrong Touching.

9. Promise **not** to hurt or touch the other person again (but only if you really mean it and want to keep your promise).

10. Sign your name.

Assignment 13A

Look at the list of things that should be in the letter. Read Kaitlyn's letter again. Write the number of each item on the list next to where that item is in Kaitlyn's letter. For example, put a number 1 next to the date in Kaitlyn's letter.

Are all the things on the list in Kaitlyn's letter? Did Kaitlyn leave anything out? Write down the number of anything on the list that you did not find in Kaitlyn's letter:

_____

_____

_____

_____

_____

_____

Assignment 13B

Now it is your turn to try writing a letter to a person you touched in a wrong way. Maybe you can do a better job than Kaitlyn did. Remember to write only things that are true and that you really mean. If you have not touched another person in a wrong way, maybe you can pick someone that you have hurt or bothered in some way.

Start your first letter on this page. Number each part of the letter to help you remember what to write. Don't worry if you mess up! Your counselor can give you more paper to write another copy of the letter.

Date: _____

Dear _____,

_____

_____

_____

_____

_____

Assignment 13B (continued)

_____

_____

_____

_____

_____

_____

_____

_____

_____

Sincerely,

_____

Great job! This is a very hard part of treatment. You might get to send the letter if your counselor thinks it would be a good idea. You might even get to meet with the other person and that person's counselor so you can apologize in person. Apologizing in person takes someone who is brave and strong, and usually everybody feels better afterward. Apologizing for bad or Wrong Behavior is a good thing, and it starts the healing and recovery process.

Understanding How You Have Hurt People and Apologizing for Your Wrong Touching
(open book)

Name:_____

Date:_____

13 points possible. 12 points needed for passing.

Total Score:___/13   ❑ Pass   ❑ Need more work

1. Check all of the things on this list that are good to include in a clarification or apology letter. Do not check the ones that are not appropriate. (10 points)

       ❑ Today's date

       ❑ A greeting with the person's correct name

       ❑ An apology for your Wrong Touching

       ❑ Explain how the victim made you abuse them

       ❑ Offer to pay the victim some money to make them forget what you did

       ❑ Write exactly what you did, without Thinking Errors

       ❑ Admit it if you lied or blamed the other person

       ❑ Say that your touching was your fault, not the victim's fault

❑ Explain the parts of your behavior that were the victim's fault

❑ Say what you are doing to stop your Wrong Touching

❑ Give another apology for your Wrong Touching

❑ Say what you liked about your sexual touching with the victim

❑ Say that you are working hard to **not** do Wrong Touching again

❑ Sign your name with a friendly, silly nickname to help the victim relax and be more comfortable

❑ Sign your name in a serious, polite way so the victim knows you are sincere

2. Check all the people on this list you should show your apology letter to. (3 points)

❑ Your parents, foster parents, or group home staff

❑ Other kids at your school

❑ Your counselors

❑ Your treatment group if you have one

❑ Your brother's or sister's friends

Congratulations on a job well done! Fill in your progress chart for this chapter and get a sticker or a high-five from your counselor.

Apologizing for your Wrong Touching or any wrong behavior helps start the healing and recovery process. Good Work!

HAPPY HEALTHY LIVING AHEAD

SAFETY 1

CHAPTER 14

Learning to Be a Survivor

In this chapter, you will learn how to overcome your past bad experiences and leave them in the dust on the road behind you. In *Roadmaps* we believe that *victims* are people who don't get over the bad things that happen to them. For example, a person who is shot and killed during a robbery is a true victim. No matter what, that person is dead and will not be coming back to life.

In real life, most bad experiences do not result in death. That is good news! That means that it is possible to recover from bad experiences and move on down the road of life to have many more good experiences.

Survivors are people who overcome their bad experiences and travel on to live good and healthy lives. Survivors don't let their bad experiences ruin their lives completely. Survivors get help to heal from the experiences that have hurt them in the past and then move on to live healthy lives. For example, think about a girl who breaks her arm badly but doesn't go to the doctor to get it put into

a cast. If she just leaves it alone, it might get infected and she might die. That would make her a victim. Also, if she doesn't go to a doctor, it might heal crooked, making her arm look strange and keeping her from being very strong. This would also make her a victim.

But if she goes to a doctor and gets an X-ray and a cast, her arm will heal just fine, and she will live the rest of her life without ever even noticing any difference. This will make her a Survivor. She has gotten help, she has overcome a bad experience, and she has moved on with her life.

Another example is a young boy whose mother and father used drugs and went to jail. The young boy ended up living in a foster home, because his parents were not able to stop using drugs. If the boy starts using drugs, runs away from the foster home, and gets put in kids' jail or juvenile detention (juvie), then he will be a victim because he is letting his past experiences ruin his new life. He is ending up with as many problems as his parents had.

But if this boy accepts help from his new foster parents, goes to counseling, and learns how to live a healthy life, then he will be a Survivor, because he is not letting his past bad experiences ruin his future.

Listen for a moment to Alex, a 10-year-old boy who is living in a foster home:

> I have been abused by my dad. He was controlling and mean. He said bad words to my mom. He yelled at me, and he called me names. My dad also sexually abused another boy who was older than me. I saw what he did to the boy. When I was about 5 years old, the older boy then did sexual things to me.
>
> After a while, I started doing Wrong Touching to others, including my younger sister. I am sorry about that now. When I did those things I was acting like a

victim *because* I was doing the same wrong things my dad and the older boy did to others.

Now I am a Survivor *because* I have been through counseling. *Roadmaps* helped me learn to make good choices and to talk about what happened to me. I know now that many people are abused, and it is not their fault. I have to work very hard to not be like my dad. I am not afraid of him anymore. I am working hard to not be mean to other people and to not abuse people. I am going to live in a good home soon. I am a Survivor.

Alex is a good example of a Survivor. He is working hard to overcome his past experiences and learn new, healthy ways to live his life.

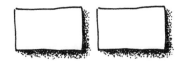

Here is a poem that Ellie wrote about herself after she was sexually abused by her stepfather. After being abused, she ended up doing Wrong Touching to her younger siblings. She had to work very hard to learn to forgive herself and love herself again. When she wrote this poem, she was feeling like a victim. The good news is that she worked very hard in her counseling, and she graduated from high school, went to college, and went on to become a Survivor. Listen to how she felt when she was younger and feeling like a victim:

Unforgettable Hatred
By Ellie Taylor

When I was a little girl,
I wanted to be a ballerina,
I wanted a dancing Barbie,
And a tuxedo Ken.
I never wanted what I got instead.
I was touched,
By someone I TRUSTED!
I have trouble trusting people now.
For this man,
I developed an unforgettable hatred.
"I will never forgive this man"
Is what I used to say.
But I am like him now.
I touched someone who trusted me.
They wanted to be just like me.
I used to say I don't hurt the people
I love.
Now,
I have developed an unforgettable
hatred...
FOR MYSELF!

Writing this poem helped Ellie feel better, and it led to her getting a lot of support from her family and friends. When Ellie learned to love herself, she became a Survivor.

Below is a description of how victims and Survivors are different.

Victims

Survivors

Victims act just like the people who abused them by abusing others.

Survivors treat others well because they care about themselves and others.

Victims do Wrong Touching because they haven't learned to care about other people.

Survivors don't ever do Wrong Touching because they think about the consequences for themselves and others.

Victims see themselves as bad people so they do wrong or bad things.

Survivors see themselves as good people so they try to do good things.

Victims feel like victims and they feel that they can't control their lives.

Survivors feel like Survivors and they know that they can control their lives in a healthy way.

Victims sometimes act helpless and they blame others for their behavior, even when the abuse is no longer happening.

Survivors admit to their mistakes and they take positive action to take charge of their lives in good ways.

Victims use lots of Thinking Errors to make excuses for their bad behavior.

Survivors don't use Thinking Errors. Instead, they take responsibility for their mistakes.

Victims may ignore rules and guidelines. Other people have to control them.

Survivors follow rules and guidelines on their own. They don't need other people to control them.

Victims have poor boundaries. They don't pay attention to the boundaries of others and they often break the boundaries of others.

Survivors have good boundaries. They understand what it feels like to have their boundaries violated so they don't violate anyone else's boundaries.

Victims don't think about the consequences of their behavior. They just do whatever they feel like.

Survivors think before acting to avoid negative consequences.

Victims may act out in wrong ways like stealing or taking things without permission, damaging property, or hitting others.

Survivors solve problems and conflicts without violence. Survivors don't hurt other people on purpose.

Victims might be too passive or they might be too aggressive.

Survivors are assertive. They say how they feel and what they want without hurting or scaring others.

Victims are often depressed and they don't care about what happens to them.

Survivors get help for their depression and they learn positive ways to make themselves feel better.

Victims don't know how to express their feelings without hurting themselves or others and they get trapped in anger and self-pity.

Survivors express themselves without hurting others or themselves by talking, exercising, drawing, or writing.

Victims have low self-esteem. They might try to hurt themselves because they don't think they are worth anything.

Survivors have high self-esteem. They know that they are not responsible for their bad childhood experiences.

Victims don't take care of themselves because they believe nobody will like them.

Survivors take good care of themselves. They have good hygiene, and they care about how they look.

Victims sometimes focus too much on sex and sexual behavior, like being sexual with too many people, or getting addicted to pornography. Their sexual life is not balanced. Sex takes on too big a role in their lives.

Survivors understand that sex can be a good, healthy part of a person's life when they're an adult, but that too much focus on sexuality can lead to trouble.

Victims focus on their own pain and draw negative attention to themselves.

Survivors can focus on other people's hurts and use their experiences to help others. Survivors give compliments, and they know how to make others feel good in healthy ways.

Victims tend to have negative behaviors that lead to failure.

Survivors work toward learning healthy and positive behaviors that lead to success.

Assignment 14A

Read the situations below, and then decide if the person is acting like a victim or a Survivor.

1. Alanna lives in a foster home. She had a hard childhood, and her parents didn't take very good care of her. Sometimes she had to go to the store to steal food for herself and her brothers. Recently, while living in the foster home, she went into a store and stole a CD so she could listen to some music.

   ❏ Alanna is acting like a Survivor   ❏ Alanna is acting like a victim

2. Tom is 11 years old, and he has seen a lot of fights and violence during his childhood. His father is in jail, and he hasn't seen his mother in a long time. One day at school another boy calls his mother a very bad name and says that he wants to fight Tom. Tom tells the boy to go away and goes to the teacher to get some support for what just happened.

   ❏ Tom is acting like a Survivor   ❏ Tom is acting like a victim

3. Lois grew up with her mother, who used drugs and had many different boyfriends. She even saw her mother have sex with lots of different men. Now that she is 11 years old, she thinks that she is old enough to have sex, and she often tries to get boys to have sex with her.

   ❏ Lois is acting like a Survivor   ❏ Lois is acting like a victim

Assignment 14A (continued)

4. Bob was touched in sexual ways by his father when he was about 6 years old. After that he did some Wrong Touching with other children. Now that he is 12 years old, he has started showing his private parts to other boys so that they will want to touch him.

❑ Bob is acting like a Survivor   ❑ Bob is acting like a victim

5. Gina is 8 years old. She was touched in her private parts by her older cousin. She has talked with her counselor about what happened, and she knows that it wasn't her fault. She has learned about Right Touching and Wrong Touching, and she is telling her counselor when she gets sexual feelings.

❑ Gina is acting like a Survivor   ❑ Gina is acting like a victim

Children are always learning and growing. Sometimes children feel like victims, and they think they will always be victims. This is not true! Being a victim or being a Survivor usually depends on how you act now—not what happened to you in the past. When children are growing up they sometimes act like victims, and they sometimes act like Survivors. A big goal in *Roadmaps* is to always work toward taking the right road to being a Survivor.

Here's what Kobe, an 11-year-old boy in a group home, has to say about his experience:

> Usually I act most like a victim. I sometimes run away, I call people names, I
> lie and steal, and I get into fights. I also used to do Wrong Touching of people's

private parts, including my younger brother and sister. Now I am sorry I made those bad choices. Now I have learned from my mistakes, and I am working every day to be a Survivor.

Kobe has learned a very important lesson. That lesson is that your past abuse doesn't decide your future. Kobe has choices to make every day. When he makes poor choices, he becomes more of a victim. When he makes good choices, he becomes more of a Survivor. Kobe's goal is to be a Survivor and to live a happy and healthy life.

Kobe has made a list of his victim and Survivor behaviors, so that he can work on doing less of the victim behaviors and more of the Survivor behaviors. Here is his list:

Kobe's Victim Behaviors:

I talk too much about sex.

I run away when I am mad.

I miss my family and I give up and think that nothing matters.

I argue a lot with adults and I use excuses.

I start fights and call people names under my breath.

Kobe's Survivor Behaviors:

I am nice to people.

I work hard in my counseling.

I take showers and I brush and floss my teeth every day.

I haven't run away in a month.

I use good manners and I follow rules.

I tell the truth, even about my mistakes.

Now it is time for you to look at your own behavior and make a list of your victim and Survivor behaviors.

Assignment 14B

In the spaces below, describe some of your behaviors from the past year. Describe some things you have done that are victim behaviors. Describe some other things you have done that are Survivor behaviors. After doing this assignment, you will have a better idea about how to practice more Survivor behaviors and fewer victim behaviors. You and your counselor can then set some goals for getting rid of your victim behaviors and doing more Survivor behaviors.

Victim behaviors:

1._____

2._____

3._____

4._____

5._____

Survivor behaviors:

1._____

2._____

Assignment 14B (continued)

3._____

4._____

5._____

Great job! Learning to be a Survivor can be very hard work. You are definitely on the right road!

SURVIVOR

In chapter 11, "Talking About Touching That People Have Done to You," you were asked about any Wrong Touching that ever happened to you. In this chapter, you will get a chance to act like a Survivor by telling someone who has hurt you in the past that you didn't like it. This is a big step toward becoming a Survivor. You'll want to start by getting your counselor's help in deciding which person in your life has hurt you the most. The person you pick might be someone who touched you in sexual ways or it might be someone who hurt you in other ways.

Assignment 14C

In the space below, write down the name of 1 person who hurt you, what the person did to you, how the experience affected you then, and how the experience still affects you now. If you want, you can use more pages to describe other people and what they did as well. If you don't know the person's name, just describe who the person was.

Person who hurt you (You can use the person's name, or you can say something like "the foster mother in the green house"):

_____

What the person did to me: _____

_____

_____

_____

_____

How that experience affected you then:

_____

_____

_____

_____

Assignment 14C (continued)

How that experience still affects you now:

_____

_____

_____

Remembering bad experiences is almost never fun. This part of *Roadmaps* takes hard work, and you are doing it. You are learning to be a Survivor. Facing your bad past experiences is part of making a new, healthy road.

Keep up the good work, you are brave!

SURVIVOR

Now we will decide what to do with those bad memories. What would you say if you could tell the person who touched you or hurt you how you felt about it? What would you want that person to say or do? Even when the other person is not in your life anymore, it might be a good idea to try to tell the person about your feelings about what was done to you. You can do this in a letter. Maybe you will want to send the letter, or maybe you won't. Your counselor will help you decide this. For now, start by trying to get your feelings down on paper, and your counselor can help

you decide later what you should do with the letter. Here's what you could put in the letter:

1. Start with a greeting, like "Hello, Billy."

2. Write how old you are now, and where you are living (not your address, but something like, "I live with my Aunt Jane now," or "I live in a group home now").

3. Say what you remember about what the person did to touch you or to hurt you.

4. Say how you felt when it was happening.

5. Tell the other person what you want him or her to do (for example, "I want you to stop touching kids and get help" or "I want you to stop hitting people").

6. Sign the letter with your name.

Here is a letter Marcus wrote to his older half-sister, who had done sexual touching with him.

August 15, 2007

Dear Beth,

I am 9 years old right now, and I am living in the Smith foster home. I can't live with Aunt Debbie anymore because I did Wrong Touching with Sara and Lisa. I remember that I learned about touching from you when I was 4 years old. You were about 8 or 9 years old. I can remember that we were at Dad's old house in the city. I can remember that we were in the blueberry patch

together, then in the bedroom together. I remember that I had to go to the bathroom. You told me that I could put my peepee in your peepee. I think you wanted to keep my peepee in your peepee longer than I did. I remember that it happened 2 times in 1 day.

I really don't know how I felt about it back then. Right now I don't feel very good about what you did to me.

I want you to stop touching kids. I think you should go to a counselor too, to get help. I also want to know why you touched me in the private parts.

Thank you for listening to my feelings. I do care about you since you are my sister.

Your brother,

Marcus

Now it is your turn to write a letter to a person who touched you or hurt you in some other way. Your counselor will help you decide who you should write the letter to. Remember, the main purpose of the letter is to help you get your feelings out.

Your counselor will also help you decide if you should send the letter or not. If you are in a treatment group, it is a good idea to share the letter with other group members. If it is the right thing for everyone, your counselor may even help you meet with the person who hurt you so that you can talk about your feelings in person. Those meetings only happen when you feel very safe.

Assignment 14D

Follow the 6 parts of writing a letter that were described earlier on page 212. In the space below, write a letter to someone who has touched you or hurt you in some way.

Date:_____

Dear _____,

_____

_____

_____

_____

_____

_____

_____

_____

Assignment 14D (continued)

_____

_____

_____

_____

_____

_____

_____

_____

_____

_____

Wow, that was a lot of work. Whether you send the letter or not, just writing it is part of the healing process.

Assignment 14E

Now share your letter with someone you trust. If you are in a treatment group for people with touching problems, you may also share it with them. Ask a person you shared the letter with to write down what they liked about it in the space below.

Person's Name: _____

What the person liked about the letter:

_____

_____

_____

_____

Congratulations! You have come down a long road. You started *Roadmaps* with many victim behaviors, but by now you are learning to be a Survivor. Staying a Survivor can sometimes take hard work because as we grow older we sometimes don't take good care of ourselves and we fall back into negative behavior patterns. It is just like if you were a car. Without regular maintenance and oil changes, even the best car will break down and stop running. Reviewing this chapter might be your own personal tune-up. You might need to come back to this chapter to set new goals, to stop your victim behaviors, and to keep your Survivor behaviors going strong.

Learning to Be a Survivor
(open book)

Name:_____

Date:_____

10 points possible. 9 points needed for passing.

Total Score:___/10   ❏ Pass   ❏ Need more work

1. Once you have been a victim, you are always a victim. (1 point)
   ❏ True   ❏ False

2. Survivors don't let their past bad experiences ruin their lives. (1 point)
   ❏ True   ❏ False

3. List 1 example of a victim behavior. (1 point)

1)_____

4. List 2 examples of Survivor behaviors. (2 points)

1)_____

2)_____

5. A person's past abuse always determines how their future will turn out.
   (1 point)

   ❏ True   ❏ False

6. Check all the things on this list that you would do when acting like a
   Survivor. (4 points)

   ❏ Express your feelings in healthy ways

   ❏ Hit someone when they make you mad

   ❏ Abuse others when they deserve it

   ❏ Think before you act and make good choices

   ❏ See yourself as a good person and try to do good things

   ❏ Take good care of your body

   ❏ Use lots of drugs and alcohol to take your mind off your
     bad past experiences

Fill in your progress
chart for this chapter
and get a sticker or a
high-five from your
counselor!

CHAPTER 15

Recognizing Your Early Warning Signs and Using Your Umbrellas

Did you ever know somebody who always seemed to have problems and kept doing wrong or bad things over and over again? Did you ever know somebody who always seemed to be in trouble? Did you ever know somebody who seemed to be stuck in repeating hurtful behaviors?

In this chapter, you will learn some new ways to make good changes in your life. Instead of getting stuck repeating Wrong Touching or other hurtful behaviors, *Roadmaps* will show you how to learn from your mistakes and make new choices. First, we'll use a lot of your new

Survivor skills from chapter 14 to figure out what we call the *Early Warning Signs* of your most difficult behaviors. Then we'll help you find some *Umbrellas* to protect you

against life's rainstorms. Umbrellas are good and safe behaviors that you can choose in hard times instead of doing things that hurt you and hurt others.

One of the best ways to not get stuck in repeating hurtful behaviors is to spot them coming and change directions. In *Roadmaps* we call this spotting your Early Warning Signs.

What if you saw a big swarm of hornets heading right toward you? Would you run out to meet it or turn the other way?

What if the sky turned dark with a funnel-shaped cloud on the horizon and you could hear the load roaring of the tornado? Would you walk right into the storm or run for cover?

What if you saw you were about to do Wrong Touching? Would you go ahead and do the Wrong Touching and risk hurting another person or going to kids' jail? Or would you use all the things you have learned in *Roadmaps* to make different choices?

Early Warning Signs, for Wrong Touching or any other problem behavior, are like spotting hornets or tornadoes up ahead. If you can see the danger, you can turn around and go the other way. You can make a better choice, one that's good and safe for you and for others. Learning to spot your Early Warning Signs is like knowing to check the skies for dark clouds and always being prepared to bring out your umbrella when it starts to rain cats and dogs!

An Early Warning Sign is anything you feel or think or do that signals that you are heading toward Wrong Sexual Behavior. Early Warning Signs are different for each boy or girl. For example, thinking about a younger child's private parts might be a signal that you would like to touch the child's private parts. That would definitely be an Early Warning Sign.

Learning to spot Early Warning Signs is an important step in learning to keep yourself and others safe. Once you can spot your

Early Warning Signs, you can take strong, positive steps to change your behavior. You can be in control of your own life and make good choices. If you learn to spot your problem behaviors early, you will be able to change them before you get into lots of trouble and end up someplace like kids' jail.

In chapter 9, "Understanding the 4 Wrong Turns to Wrong Touching," you took a look at things that happened to you in your life that played a part in your getting a Bad Map. By now, you probably have a pretty good idea of where you got your Bad Map or where you learned about Wrong Touching. You might even be beginning to understand why you have done Wrong Touching in the past. The next step in learning to be a Survivor, building a new Good Map, and overcoming your Roadblocks is to find your own Early Warning Signs. This is a lot like driving on a new road and watching for dangerous

turns. On each turn you then put up a big yellow CAUTION, SLOW DOWN sign. This will always warn you of the dangerous turn. With Wrong Touching problems, your Early Warning Signs will be just like those yellow CAUTION, SLOW DOWN signs. They will help you stay safe and have good behavior.

Let's start by looking at your life and the lives of other kids with touching problems and try to figure out your Early Warning Signs for Wrong Touching.

Remember Buzzbee's friends Rita, Ted, Amber, and Bryan from

earlier chapters? They each did a lot of work with their counselors to figure out some of the Early Warning Signs for Wrong Touching. They started by trying to remember some of the things that were happening in their lives when they did the Wrong Touching. Some of the things they remembered were being touched sexually by older persons, moving into a foster home, seeing other people having sex, watching sexy movies, seeing pictures of naked people on the Internet, getting in trouble all the time, or feeling lonely, sad, or mad all the time.

As they thought back to those times in their lives, their counselors helped them find some of the Early Warning Signs for their Wrong Touching. Here are some of the things they came up with:

I started touching my own private parts all the time.

I felt like giving up, and I didn't care about what I was doing.

I started thinking a lot about naked bodies and private part touching.

I started thinking more about touching other people in their privates.

I kept sneaking around to get on the Internet so I could look at the pictures of naked people.

I started talking more to other people about sex and I asked lots of sexual questions.

I would try to get close to people so I could touch them.

I drew lots of pictures of private parts.

I cut out lots of pictures of naked people and hid them in my room.

I would take underwear from the laundry and put it in my bedroom.

I would try to get close to people so I could rub up against them.

I would pretend to rub my privates while other kids were watching.

I would ask all my friends for magazines or pictures of naked people.

Now it is time to think about your own Wrong Touching problems. In this next assignment, you will be asked to come up with a list of things that you think might tell you that you are about to do Wrong Touching. To do this assignment, you have to think back to when your touching problems started, then think about the thoughts, feelings, and behaviors you had that might have led you to do Wrong Touching. This list will be different for every person.

Assignment 15A

In the space below, make a list of the thoughts, feelings, or behaviors that might be Early Warning Signs for your Wrong Sexual Behavior. You might want to ask your counselor for help with this assignment.

_____

_____

_____

_____

_____

_____

_____

Great job! You worked hard, and you really thought about it. Learning to spot Early Warning Signs is not always easy. But learning to spot your Early Warning Signs can keep you out of lots of trouble!

Do not ignore Early Warning Signs. Ask for help when bad things happen to you, or when you feel bad.

This might be a good place to take a break from all this hard work. When you and your counselor are ready, go ahead and continue where you left off.

As you learned earlier, learning to spot your Early Warning Signs is like knowing to check the skies for dark clouds overhead. This way you will always be prepared to bring out your umbrella when it starts to rain cats and dogs! In real life, umbrellas protect us from the rain. In *Roadmaps* Umbrellas are positive, healthy behaviors that protect us from life's rainstorms. Umbrellas are things that you can do when you spot dark clouds overhead—your Early Warning Signs—to help you get past bad times, bad thoughts, and bad feelings by making good choices. Umbrellas get you out of problem behaviors and send you in a positive, healthy direction.

Here is a general list of positive behaviors that help young people when they have problems in their lives. In *Roadmaps* we call these positive behaviors Umbrellas. You might find some good ideas from this list that will help you with your problems!

Ask for help.

Talk to someone you trust about your feelings.

Tell your parent, counselor, or group home
staff member what is bothering you.

Ask a friend to listen to your problems.

Write down your feelings in a diary or journal.

Get some healthy exercise.

Spend some time outside, with nature.

Listen to a book on tape to relax.

Take a nap so you wake up ready to make good choices.

Use positive self-talk. Tell yourself that you can make good choices.

Write down some positive goals on a piece of paper.

Take a shower and brush your teeth so that you feel clean and good.

Do something healthy that makes you feel good, like paint a
picture, read a book, or write a poem.

Do something nice for another person.

Tell yourself to remember that you are a Survivor, not a victim.

Now it's time to figure out what kinds of Umbrellas will work for
you. You can use the above list to get you started. But what is most
important is figuring out what works for you. You are special and have
your own likes and dislikes. You probably know better than anybody
else what can stop you from feeling bad and doing Wrong Behavior.
You probably know better than anybody else what makes you happy.
So you'll want to come up with your own ideas about what puts you in
a better mood when times are hard.

Assignment 15B

In the space below, make a list of your Umbrellas—all the positive and healthy things you can do when you notice that you are having bad thoughts or bad feelings. List as many as you can. If you have more ideas, you can ask your counselor for more paper.

_____

_____

_____

_____

_____

_____

_____

_____

_____

_____

Now let's work on finding good Umbrellas to keep you from doing Wrong Touching. Let's start by looking at the Umbrellas that Rita, Ted, Amber, and Bryan came up with to help them react in a positive way to some of their Early Warning Signs:

Early Warning Sign: I started touching my own private parts all the time.

Umbrella: I started trying to exercise more instead of just touching my private parts.

Early Warning Sign: I felt like giving up, and I didn't care about what I was doing.

Umbrella: I talked with my counselor, and we figured out why I was sad. We made some plans to help me feel better.

Early Warning Sign: I started thinking a lot about naked bodies and private part touching.

Umbrella: I tried to think about what would happen if I went to kids' jail, and that helped me stop thinking about naked bodies so much.

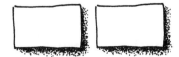

Early Warning Sign: I started thinking more about touching other people in their privates.

Umbrella: I told my counselor and he taught me about what was legal and illegal or against the law, and he taught me about all the bad things that can happen if I touched someone's private parts.

Early Warning Sign: I kept sneaking around to get on the Internet so I could look at the pictures of naked people.

Umbrella: I told my foster mother, and she put a password on the computer so I wouldn't be so tempted. She also told me that a lot of what I was seeing on the Internet wasn't real, and that it gave me wrong ideas about sexual behavior.

Early Warning Sign: I started talking more to other people about sex and I asked lots of sexual questions.

Umbrella: My counselor explained to me that by talking about sex with other people I could get into trouble for sexual harassment. My counselor and my foster parents told me that it was OK to talk to them about my sexual questions.

Early Warning Sign: I would try to get close to people so I could touch them.

Umbrella: I learned about having a 2-foot bubble so that I always stay 2 feet away from other people, and that helps me not be so tempted to touch people.

Now it's your turn. Like Rita, Ted, Amber, and Bryan, you'll want to think about your own Early Warning Signs and come up with an Umbrella that will really work for each one of them. You'll want to find Umbrellas that help you choose healthy and helpful behaviors in difficult times instead of acting on urges that hurt you or hurt others. You will need to decide what works for you, since everyone is different.

Assignment 15C

Using the space below, first write down all your Early Warning Signs from Assignment 15A. Then come up with at least one Umbrella for each of your Early Warning Signs. Make sure that you pick an Umbrella that will really work for that particular Early Warning Sign. You might want to ask your counselor for help.

Early Warning Sign _____

Umbrella _____

Early Warning Sign _____

Umbrella _____

Assignment 15C (continued)

Early Warning Sign _____

Umbrella _____

Early Warning Sign _____

Umbrella _____

Early Warning Sign _____

Umbrella _____

Early Warning Sign _____

Umbrella _____

Early Warning Sign _____

Umbrella _____

Early Warning Sign _____

Umbrella _____

Now let's take what you've learned about Early Warning Signs and
Umbrellas and apply it to other kinds of problems besides Wrong
Touching. Here are some problems that other kids have worked on:

Angie gets mad at staff where she lives and she often ends up yelling bad things.

Billy has problems getting along with other kids, and he starts a lot of fights by calling them names.

Suzanne steals things from other people at school.

With help from their counselors and parents, Angie, Billy, and Suzanne recognized that they were getting stuck in these bad behaviors and repeating them over and over. They each figured out some of their Early Warning Signs and made a list of helpful things that worked as Umbrellas to help them stay on the right path. Here is what Angie, Billy, and Suzanne learned:

Problem behavior: Angie gets mad at staff where she lives and she often ends up yelling bad things.

Early Warning Signs: Angie realized that she was very unhappy that she had to live in a group home, and she really felt very alone. She learned that her unhappy feelings were her Early Warning Signs.

Umbrellas: Angie finds that talking to staff about her feelings helped her feel better every day. She also finds that she doesn't get as mad if she keeps telling herself positive things. This is called using positive self-talk.

Problem behavior: Billy has problems getting along with other kids, and he starts a lot of fights by calling them names.

Early Warning Signs: Billy learned that he was very negative with other people, and that he tended to start fights when he did not get to talk with his mother on the phone. He also learned that when he did poorly in school, he got into more fights. So his Early Warning Signs were not getting to talk to his mother and getting bad grades on assignments and tests in school.

Umbrellas: Billy realizes that his mother has disappointed him all his life, and that he feels better when he focuses on more positive parts of his life, like looking forward to

a fun activity. He also realizes that he has some good subjects in school that made him feel good. His Umbrellas are keeping his mind on positive activities and telling himself that he is going to have a good life with the things he is good at.

Problem behavior: Suzanne steals things from other people at school.

Early Warning Signs: Suzanne learned that when she didn't take her medication, she made poor choices. She also learned that she tended to steal things when she felt bad about herself, or lonely, and didn't talk to others. These were all her Early Warning Signs.

Umbrellas: Suzanne realizes that she needs to take her medication every day, and that she feels less lonely when she spends time with other people. Her Umbrellas are taking her medication, spending time around other caring persons, and talking to adults about her feelings.

What are some of your other problem behaviors? Do you get mad all the time? Do you not want to share the stuff you like to play with or read with anyone else? Do you get into fights? Do you break things? Do you throw your clothes and stuff on the floor? Do you lie to adults? Do you steal things from others? Let's see if we can find ways to understand and change some other negative behavior patterns using what we've learned in this chapter.

Assignment 15D

List some problem behaviors you have had in the past year or 2. They don't have to be sexual problem behaviors—they can be any problem behaviors.

_____

_____

Assignment 15D (continued)

_____

_____

_____

_____

Assignment 15E

You will probably want your counselor's help to work on this assignment. First choose 3 of your problem behaviors from Assignment 15D and write them in the spaces below. Next find at least one Early Warning Sign for each problem behavior. Then write down what would work as Umbrellas for each of the problem behaviors and Early Warning Signs.

Problem behavior _____

Early Warning Signs _____

Umbrellas _____

_____

_____

Assignment 15E (continued)

Problem behavior _____

Early Warning Signs _____

Umbrellas _____

_____

_____

Problem behavior _____

Early Warning Signs _____

Umbrellas _____

_____

_____

Changing your problem behaviors can take time and lots of effort. In this chapter, you have learned to pay attention to your Early Warning Signs that lead to trouble. You have learned that Umbrellas are positive steps you can take to protect you from problem behaviors, just like umbrellas help protect you from rainstorms. You have also learned that paying attention to your Early Warning Signs and using your Umbrellas can help you with lots of different behavior problems. Now it is up to you to watch for problem behaviors and put up your Umbrellas when you see any Early Warning Signs.

Here comes a rain storm. I better turn on my wipers.

ROAD TEST 15

Recognizing Your Early Warning Signs and Using Your Umbrellas
(closed book–do this from memory)

Name:_____

Date:_____

12 points possible. 11 points needed for passing.

Total Score:___/12   ❑ Pass   ❑ Need more work

1. An Early Warning Sign is: (1 point)

       A.___ something that forces you to do wrong things.

       B.___ a behavior, feeling, or thought that helps lead you to
            problem behavior.

       C.___something you should ignore.

       D.___ a red road sign that tells you to stop ahead.

2. Everybody does some negative behaviors during their lifetime. (1 point)
     ❑ True   ❑ False

3. In order to change your problem behaviors, you have to pay attention to: (1 point)

A.___Pokemon.

B.___Early Warning Signs.

C.___the TV.

D.___porno movies and pictures.

4. List 3 Early Warning Signs that might lead you to do more Wrong Touching. (3 points)

1)_____

2)_____

3)_____

5. Check all the things in this list that are good, positive ways to "put up your Umbrella" to help you make good choices and stay out of trouble. (5 points)

❑ Hit something hard to get your feelings out

❑ Look at a picture of a naked person to get your mind off of what is bothering you

❑ Talk to someone about your feelings

❏ Get some healthy exercise

❏ Do something mean to someone else to get your feelings out

❏ Listen to a book on tape to relax

❏ Ask a friend to listen to your problems

❏ Write in your diary how you feel

6. Learning to spot Early Warning Signs: (1 point)

A.___is something only adults can do.

B.___is an important step in learning to keep yourself and others safe.

C.___is something you learn in college.

D.___is important for cats and dogs.

Good job on this test and this chapter! Fill in your progress chart and get a sticker or a high-five from your counselor.

Learning to spot life's rainstorms and use your Umbrellas keeps you on the road to healthy adventures and a happy life!

HAPPY HEALTHY LIVING AHEAD

SAFETY 1

CHAPTER 16

Making and Using Your Safety Plan Book

Congratulations on making it this far in *Roadmaps!* You are very close to becoming a full member of the Sexual Abuse Prevention and Safety Team. Not only that, but you are also learning to be a Survivor and live a happy and healthy life!

Now is the time to put everything you have learned together and share it with other people on your support team. You have one more fun assignment to do. This one will bring out the best in you and you will have a chance to be creative. In this chapter, you will review everything you have learned in *Roadmaps* and make a Safety Plan Book.

A Safety Plan is a plan for making your life safe and healthy. A Safety Plan has all the steps you need to keep thinking, feeling, and behaving in safe and healthy ways. Your Safety Plan will contain rules and guidelines to keep everyone safe. A Safety Plan is like a good, solid guardrail that keeps you from driving off a cliff on a narrow mountain road. The guardrail keeps you safe and keeps you on the road. If your guardrail is not strong enough, you might go off the road and fall down the cliff and hurt yourself or others.

Your Safety Plan Book will contain all the different parts of your personal Safety Plan. It is a notebook of helpful rules, reminders, and ideas about how you can stay safe and make good choices. Your Safety Plan Book is also a summary of what you have learned in *Roadmaps*. It will have lots of different pages that you will continue to look at and add to long after you finish *Roadmaps*. Your Safety Plan Book is your own personal guardrail. By making it strong and solid, you will stay safe and make all the right turns.

You can take your Safety Plan Book with you no matter where you go. You can add to it, you can change it, and, best of all, you can share it with your support team—people who care about you and want to help you keep on the road to a healthy and happy life.

Your support team is made up of the people you can talk to about your Wrong Touching problem. Some of your support team members will be family members and others will be counselors, group home staff members, or other people who spend time with you. Having a support team is like having a navigation system or good map in your car. Those things keep you from making wrong turns and keep you on the road to good adventures.

Do you want to hear some good news? There is no road test for this chapter. The final exam is to make your Safety Plan Book and for you to keep practicing everything you have learned in *Roadmaps*. Making it through *Roadmaps* is only the first part of your journey. The next step is to keep using everything you have learned. If you forget what you have learned, you might start making wrong turns and getting into trouble. If you keep practicing everything you have learned, you will become a true Survivor, and you will be a happy and healthy person.

Let's start your Safety Plan Book now! If your counselor has already gotten you started on your Safety Plan Book that is good news. If you haven't gotten started yet, now is a great time to begin!

Don't be shy—this is your Safety Plan Book. Do your best, and everyone will be proud of you. It is OK to ask for help too. Sometimes even I need to call a tow truck when I get stuck.

To start making your Safety Plan Book, you'll need these supplies:

    3-ring notebook

    plastic sheet holders

You might also want to use:

    crayons, colored pencils, or colored markers

    stickers or other things to decorate your pages like

       old post cards or pictures cut out of magazines

    colored construction paper

    glue or tape

    scissors

    3-hole punch

    stapler

Ask a grownup for help in getting supplies.

For each assignment in this chapter, begin by asking your counselor to photocopy and 3-hole punch the assignment for you. That way you will have a separate page to work on that you can decorate and color as much as you like and then put right into your Safety Plan Book. Make sure to put each page inside a plastic sheet cover.

Now it is time to start having fun! This is a creative assignment and your job is to be creative and make this your Safety Plan Book. This means that you can decorate it any way you would like, so that you will be proud of what you have done and so that you will enjoy looking at your Safety Plan Book and sharing it with others. You can use the pages provided, or you can use the ideas and information in each assignment to design your own page.

We'll start by making a cover page. Then we'll take some time to look back at what you've learned in *Roadmaps*, chapter by chapter. Each time you complete an assignment, decorate it so you like how it looks, and add it to your Safety Plan Book. You can also add other kinds of pages—as many as you would like. If you have learned new skills during your work in *Roadmaps*, you can put those on separate pages and add them to your Safety Plan Book as well. For example, one boy put up a poster on his refrigerator that said: JUST TALK ABOUT YOUR FEELINGS. That turned out to be

a very good page to put in his Safety Plan Book as a reminder of what he learned. You can add other things that you've learned in *Roadmaps* other assignments that were important to you, poems or stories you've written, or pictures you've drawn. Once you're all done, you and your counselor can rearrange the materials and decide what else you might want to include. Deciding what to put in your Safety Plan Book is up to you and your counselor. It's your book!

Remember, you may need to take a break after each step or at any other time if you get tired. This project may take some time, but don't worry about it — you are on the way to a healthy life.

You've come a long way in *Roadmaps*, and your Safety Plan Book is something you can take along with you as you continue your journey beyond *Roadmaps* to a happy and healthy life.

My Book Cover

Every book needs a cover! Covers tell us the book's title and the name of the author—you! Some covers have nice designs and some have illustrations that tell us something about the book.

Make a cover for your Safety Plan Book that includes a title, your name, and any decorations you like. Glue your cover to the outside of your 3-ring notebook. Here is Buzzbee's cover as an example.

My Author Bio

First, write a short bio. A few sentences will do. Then add a picture or drawing of yourself. When you're done, glue your author bio onto the inside back cover of your 3-ring notebook. Here is Buzzbee's author bio as an example.

Buzzbee lives in Washington State. He loves basketball, playing the kazoo, and driving around. Buzzbee has a pet dog named Max. This is his first book.

Survivor Kid Press

My Title Page

A book's title page gives the title, the name of the author, and the name of the publisher.

Make a title page for your Safety Plan Book that includes a title, your name, and a made-up publisher.

Buzzbee has shared his titled page to help you with some ideas.

My Safety Plan Book

Buzzbee's Really Great Tips
for
Staying Safe and Healthy

by

Buzzbee

Survivor Kid Press

My Dedication Page

A great way to start a book is with a dedication page. This is where you thank people who have helped you in your counseling. This could include parents, other relatives, foster parents, group home staff, or counselors.

Here is an example of a dedication page one 10-year-old boy wrote for his Safety Plan Book.

Ask your counselor to type for you and make up your own thank you to everyone who has helped you. Sign your name at the bottom of the page. Put your dedication page in your Safety Plan Book, right after your title page.

Dedication

I want to thank my mom, my dad, my stepmom, my counselor, my sister, Jen, and my brother, Hanrick, and my grandma for helping me to make good choices. I would also like to thank my aunt, McKenna, and my uncles, Todd and Jerry, and my cousins, Sam, Jenny, Rick, and Erin, for helping to take care of me. My promise is to put family first and friends next and to grow up to be a person of integrity.

Eddie, March 2007

Being Me in a Happy, Healthy Life

What does it mean to be yourself and live a happy, healthy life? Each person's answers are different, because each one of us is special and different. To think about this question, go back and review chapter 1, "Start Your Engines." In that chapter, you shared some things about yourself.

For your Safety Plan Book, answer the following questions about being yourself in a happy, healthy life.

I am good at: _____

_____

_____ .

My favorite activities are: _____

_____

_____ .

When I grow up I want to be a: _____

_____

_____ .

The person I want to be most like when I grow

up is:_____

_____

_____ .

My best qualities are: _____

_____

_____ .

When I get upset, I express my feelings by

talking to: _____

_____

_____ .

When I get mad, I do many healthy things, like:

_____

_____

_____ .

Here Is My Support Team!

Go back and review what you learned in chapter 2. In that chapter, you learned about touching problems. You also learned about having a Support Team—people you can talk to when you are feeling mad, sad, or having sexual feelings.

For your Safety Plan Book, add a face and hair to show each person on your Support Team. Then fill in each person's name tag.

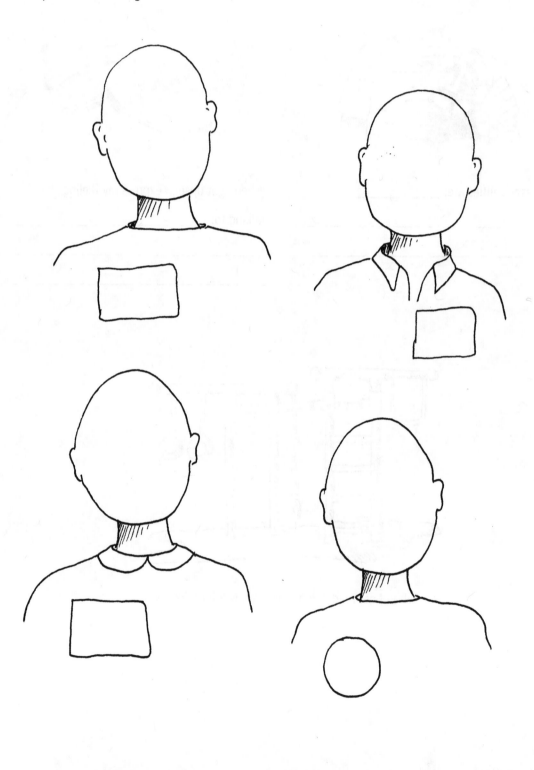

These are all the people I can tell when I am feeling mad, sad, or upset, or when I am having sexual feelings. I want to thank each of the people here for helping me in my life.

A Picture of Me in My Healthy Life

In chapter 2, you also learned about how to act in groups, you made a problem list, and you drew some pictures of yourself and others.

For your Safety Plan Book, draw a picture of yourself doing some healthy activity that makes you happy.

Understanding the Anger Iceberg

Go back and review what you learned in chapter 3. In that chapter, you learned how to talk about feelings. You also learned about the anger iceberg and all the feelings people can have underneath their anger.

For your Safety Plan Book, fill in the iceberg with as many feelings as you can, to show all the different feelings people sometimes have when they feel angry.

Using Right Touching

Go back and review what you learned in chapter 4. In that chapter, you learned about Right Touching and Wrong Touching. You also learned about what is illegal and legal.

For your Safety Plan Book, think about all the good things that will happen if you stop doing Wrong Touching and only do Right Touching. Draw a picture of 6 of these good things in the frames and label each picture.

Here are good things that will happen if I stop
doing Wrong Touching and only do Right Touching.

Using Right Thinking and Avoiding Wrong Thinking

Go back and review what you learned in chapter 5. In that chapter, you learned about Right Thinking and Wrong Thinking. You also learned about Thinking Errors and positive and negative self-talk.

For your Safety Plan Book, list the Thinking Errors that you try not to use.

Here are some Thinking Errors that I try not to use.
By avoiding Thinking Errors, I will be a healthy and responsible person!

For your Safety Plan Book, list some of the positive self-talk that you use to remind yourself that you are a good person.

Here are some good things about myself that keep me on the right road and keep me feeling good about myself.

Controlling Sexual Feelings and Urges

Go back and review what you learned in chapter 6. In that chapter, you learned how to talk about and control your sexual feelings and urges.

For your Safety Plan Book, think of all the things that help you control your sexual feelings in healthy ways. Write them in the road signs below.

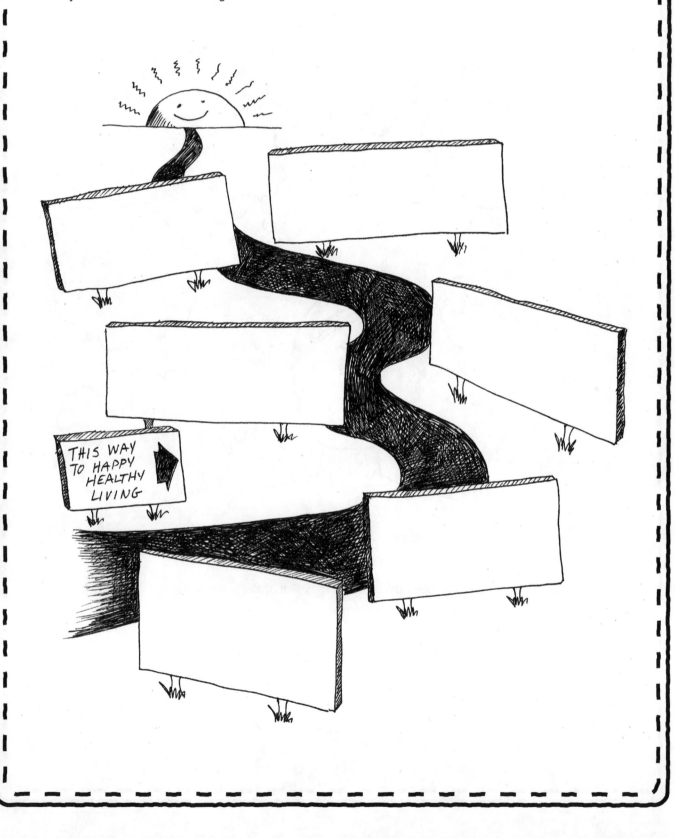

Taking Care of My Body

Go back and review what you learned in chapter 7. In that chapter, you learned about your body and puberty. Think about all the things you do every day to take good care of your body. You might want to look at Assignment 7A (on page 86) for some ideas.

For your Safety Plan Book, draw a line connecting each of the items to where it's used to keep your body well-groomed, clean, and healthy.

Staying Out of Kids' Jail

Go back and review what you learned in chapter 8. In that chapter, you learned some good rules to help you stay out of kids' jail. You also learned about Right Body Control and Wrong Body Control.

For your Safety Plan Book, make a list of all the rules you have learned that will help keep you out of kids' jail. Use the list of rules for staying out of kids' jail in chapter 8 (on pages 95 and 96) as the starting point for your new list. If you need more spaces to write in, ask your counselor for more copies of this page.

Avoiding Roadblocks and Danger Zones

Go back and review what you learned in chapter 9. In that chapter, you learned about Bad Maps, Roadblocks, and how bad choices lead to bad behavior.

For your Safety Plan Book, use the boulders on the road to list as many Roadblocks as you can. You can include people who were mean to you, activities that make you feel bad about yourself, things that get you thinking about sex or private parts, or anything at all that keeps you from a healthy life.

Avoiding Roadblocks and Danger Zones

In chapter 9, you also learned about Danger Zones—places or situations that could make it very easy to make wrong choices and do Wrong Touching. For your Safety Plan Book, write down some of the Danger Zones that you have learned to avoid. Review your list from chapter 9 and try to add any others that you have learned about since.

Keeping Good Boundaries

Go back and review what you learned in chapter 10. In that chapter, you learned about following your Special Safety Rules and respecting the boundaries of other people.

For your Safety Plan Book, first photocopy your Special Safety Rules from Assignment 10C (page 151) and decorate it any way you like. Then write down 6 things you can do to respect the boundaries of other people.

_____

_____

_____

_____

_____

_____

Sharing Feelings About Wrong Touching

Go back and review what you learned in chapter 11. In that chapter, you learned about how it feels to have people do Wrong Touching to you, and you learned how to support other people who have had Wrong Touching done to them. You also learned to talk about where you learned about sexual touching behavior.

For your Safety Plan Book, first photocopy the picture you drew for Assignment 11D (on page 171), where you drew someone touching you in a way you didn't like. Then, draw faces to show how Wrong Sexual Touching makes other people feel, and label each face with a feeling word.

Telling the Truth

Go back and review what you learned in chapter 12. In that chapter, you learned to stop keeping secrets and to talk about all the mistakes you have made in the past.

For your Safety Plan Book, make a list of all the reasons that people should tell the truth about the Wrong Touching mistakes they made in the past.

_____

_____

_____

_____

_____

_____

_____

_____

_____

_____

_____

_____

_____

Apologizing is a good start toward making things better!

Apologizing for My Wrong Touching

Go back and review what you learned in chapter 13. In that chapter, you learned how you might have hurt other people, and you learned how to apologize for your past Wrong Behavior.

For your Safety Plan Book, describe how apologizing for your past Wrong Touching helps you on the right road to a happy and healthy life.

_____

_____

_____

_____

_____

_____

_____

_____

_____

_____

_____

Acting Like a Survivor

Go back and review what you learned in chapter 14. In that chapter, you learned how to be a Survivor, not a victim.

For your Safety Plan Book, describe all of your present behaviors that are Survivor behaviors.

_____

_____

_____

_____

_____

_____

_____

_____

_____

_____

_____

SURVIVOR

I refuse to be a victim, I am going to be a Survivor, forever!

Recognizing Early Warning Signs and Using Umbrellas

Go back and review what you learned in chapter 15. In that chapter, you learned how to find your Early Warning Signs and how to put up your Umbrellas to keep from making bad choices.

For your Safety Plan Book, first make a list of all your Early Warning Signs.

Look out! Here are some behaviors that can mean I'm heading for Wrong Touching.

My Umbrellas

For your Safety Plan Book, list all the Umbrellas that help you avoid bad behavior.

_____

_____

_____

_____

_____

_____

Try these! Here are some things I can do when I have bad thoughts or bad feelings.
They help me stay positive.

Safety First

Think about how much you've learned about keeping on the right road for safety and a healthy, happy life!

For your Safety Plan Book, list all the things you have learned in *Roadmaps* to keep on the right road to happy times and good adventures. If you need more spaces to write in, ask your counselor for more copies of this page. The more guardrails you can fill in, the safer you will be!

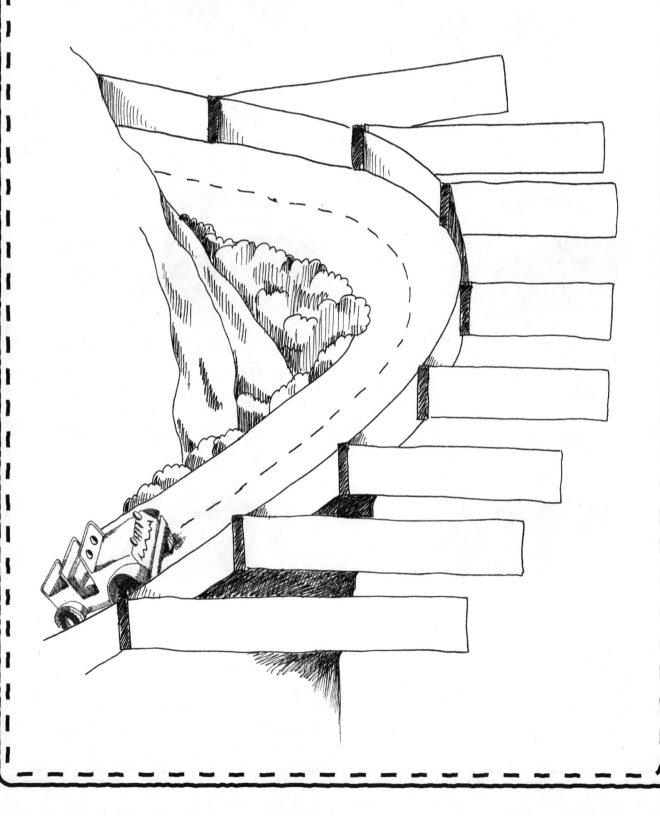

My Future, Happy, Healthy Life

Roadmaps has focused on helping you develop a happy, healthy life. Now it is time for you to describe what that will look like for you. Use your positive imagination to think about what your happy, healthy life will look like. It might be the way your life is right now, or it might be much different. This is a very personal assignment.

In the space on this page, draw a complete picture of your happy, healthy life. Include as much as you can in the picture, including your home, your family and friends, your fun interests, and maybe your school or job. This is a picture of how you would like to live in the future.

My Team Membership

Congratulations! You are now a member of the Sexual Abuse Prevention and Safety Team.

Have your counselor fill out the membership form for the Sexual Abuse Prevention and Safety Team, and then put it in as the last page in your Safety Plan Book.

Sharing My Safety Plan Book

With your counselor's help, go back and look through your Safety Plan Book one more time. If you have anything else you would like to add, do that now. Remember, the stronger your Safety Plan Book is, the safer you will be. You can also move things around in your Safety Plan Book in whatever order works best for you.

Once you and your counselor are happy with your Safety Plan book, it's time to share it with everyone on your Support Team. Go to each person on your Support Team and show them all the work you have done on your Safety Plan Book. Make sure to thank each person for helping you.

Congratulations! You have completed Roadmaps! You are a true Survivor. And you are now a member of the Sexual Abuse Prevention and Safety Team. Way to go!

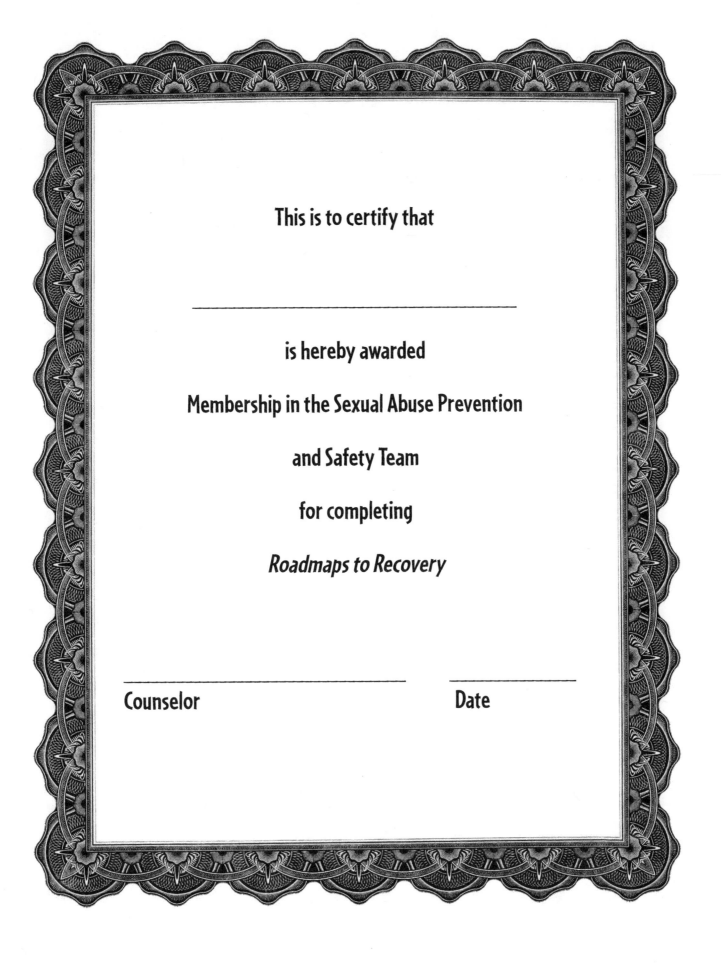

This is to certify that

_____

is hereby awarded

Membership in the Sexual Abuse Prevention

and Safety Team

for completing

Roadmaps to Recovery

_____   _____

Counselor   Date

CONGRATULATIONS!

You have finished *Roadmaps*. You have done an incredible amount of work. You have traveled a very long and difficult road. You are a Survivor. You have stayed on course, and you have avoided many Roadblocks. You now understand how to think and act like a healthy, responsible person. You also know how to share your feelings with others in a safe way. You should be proud of yourself, because you are now a member of the Sexual Abuse Prevention and Safety Team.

Remember, your Safety Plan Book is your personal roadmap to staying on the right road. You should keep it in a safe place, and you should add new pages to it as you overcome new struggles or learn new skills for living a healthy life. Go back and look at it from time to time, because that will help yo u remember to practice all the skills you have learned. Finishing *Roadmaps* is a big step toward a healthy life, but life is just beginning, and you have many other roads ahead.

Here's Buzzbee with some final words of advice.

You've got lots of good adventures ahead. Remember to keep paying attention and always take the safest road. You have worked very hard, and I am very proud of you!

Word List

abuse. When somebody does something that hurts another person.

aggressive. When people act pushy and sometimes demanding.

apology. When you say you are sorry for something you have done.

assertive. When people speak up for themselves and say what they think. Assertive people express their feelings without hurting or scaring other people.

Bad Map. Bad things that you were taught when you were young. A Bad Map can mean that you did **not** learn some of the healthy things you should have learned.

behavior. A person's actions—something they do.

body boundary. A person's private space, like how much room you want around you.

body needs. Things that you need from other people (your family and friends) that have to do with your body. Body needs are things that help us stay alive and feel strong and healthy and good.

boundaries. Something that protects something that is private, or that just belongs to you. A boundary is an invisible wall that we don't want people to cross.

circumcision. When some skin, called foreskin, is trimmed off of a boy's penis just after the boy is born.

clitoris. Sits under a little hood at the top of where the lips of a girl's private parts come together. It's about the size of a button and is very sensitive to the touch and can make a girl feel all excited inside.

consent. When someone gives their permission to do something and that person really understands what is going to happen.

consequences. The punishments or responses we get when we do something.

counselor. Someone who knows how to help kids and grownups in lots of different ways.

court. A room that is controlled by a judge, where people go to solve disagreements or to receive punishments for bad behavior.

Danger Zone. A place where you might be more likely to do Wrong Touching, or where bad things are more likely to happen.

depressed. When a person is sad, lonely, and unhappy for a long time, we say they are depressed.

Early Warning Signs. Anything you feel or think or do that signals that you are heading toward Wrong Sexual Behavior or Wrong Touching.

ejaculation. What comes out of a boy's penis when he masturbates, or has sex, and has an orgasm.

emotional needs. Things like love, compliments, and praise, that make you feel good about yourself and help you believe you are a loved and worthwhile person.

erection. The correct term for when a boy's penis gets stiff and sticks out.

goal. Something to work for that makes you feel good and strong inside yourself.

groups. When 3 or more people sit down together with a counselor to talk about their problems.

horny. A word some people use to describe having sexual feelings.

illegal. Against the law and **not** OK to do.

incest. When people who are related to each other in the same family touch each other's private parts. Incest is illegal, or against the law.

judge. A person who is in charge of a courtroom. A judge has the job of deciding what should happen to people who break the law. Judges also help settle arguments, and they make lots of other decisions. Judges even make final decisions about when a child is adopted.

juvenile detention, or juvie. Where children get sent by judges if they do something that is very wrong or hurtful. It is a place with locked doors where children have to live and follow strict rules until the judge says it is time to get out. Also called **kids' jail.**

kids' jail. Where children get sent by judges if they do something that is very wrong or very hurtful. It is a place with locked doors where children have to live and follow strict rules until the judge says it is time to get out. Also called **juvenile detention,** or **juvie.**

legal. When something is OK to do and you will **not** go to jail if you do it.

masturbation. When boys touch or rub their penises or girls touch their clitorises and it feels very good.

menstruation. A girl's monthly cycle or monthly period, when she bleeds a little from her vagina.

negative. Bad, wrong, or unhealthy things.

normal relationships. Healthy, caring friendships between people.

ovary. The part inside every girl where hundreds of thousands of eggs are stored. Girls have 2 ovaries.

passive. When people let things be done to them, or don't do anything. Passive people act like nothing is bothering them, and they don't express their feelings.

penis. A boy's private part.

periods. Another word for **menstruation.**

positive. Good or healthy things.

prevention. Keeping something from happening.

private parts. A person's bottom, chest, penis, vulva, and vagina. These are also called **sexual parts.**

problem. Something that makes your life harder, that gets you in trouble with other kids or grownups, or that makes you feel bad.

puberty. When your body changes from being a child's body into being more like an adult's.

Right Thinking. When you think healthy and responsible thoughts.

Right Touching. Healthy and good touching, when you ask before you touch, and the other person says it's OK. Touching that is legal is Right Touching.

self-esteem. How a person feels about themselves.

self-talk. What people say to themselves inside their own minds. They don't actually talk out loud—they just think to themselves.

sex. Private part touching. There are many different kinds of sex, but in *Roadmaps*, sex means private part touching.

sex offender. Any person who does Wrong Sexual Touching that is illegal, or against the law, and goes to court and gets punished by a judge.

sexual abuse. When somebody does Wrong Sexual Behavior to another person.

sexual behavior problem. When somebody touches somebody else's private parts without permission, or when the person being touched is too young to know what's going on, or when a person talks about private parts too much, or touches their own private parts too much in front of other people. Sometimes stealing another person's underwear, showing off their private parts, looking at pornography, or drawing sexy pictures can also be sexual behavior problems.

sexual harassment. When a person says or does something sexual or personal that bothers another person.

sexual parts. Parts of the body that have to do with sex. These are often called **private parts.**

sexual touching. Touching another person's private parts.

sexually transmitted diseases (STDs); sexually transmitted infections (STIs). Diseases and infections that people get mainly from doing sexual touching.

Special Safety Rules. Rules that help you stop doing Wrong Touching.

sperm. The part of a boy or a man that swims up inside a girl or a woman and joins with an egg to make a baby.

Survivor. Someone who overcomes a bad experience and doesn't let it bother them for a long time.

Thinking Errors. Thinking mistakes, or lies that we tell ourselves. Thinking Errors are a type of unhealthy self-talk. Here are some examples of Thinking Errors:

> **anger.** When you express your feelings by showing anger, instead of talking about the other feelings you are having.

blaming. When you say that someone else made you do something.

denial. When you lie or don't tell the whole truth about something, or you pretend something is not happening.

excuse making / justifying. When you make up excuses for your behavior. Also called **justifying.**

lack of empathy / me, me, me. When you only think about yourself, and you ignore how your behavior will affect other people. Also called **me, me, me.**

lying. When you say you did **not** do something that you really did do.

minimizing. When you make a Wrong Behavior seem less wrong than it really was.

never, ever, always / all-or-nothing thinking / universals. When a person uses words like *never, ever,* or *always.* Also called all-or-nothing thinking or universals.

threats. When a person says that something bad is going to happen if the other person doesn't do what they want.

touching problem. When one person touches another person without permission.

Umbrellas. All the positive and healthy things you can do when you notice that you are having bad thoughts or bad feelings.

vagina. A girl's inside private part. This is the part of the woman's body where babies come out of when they are born.

victim. Someone who doesn't get over the bad things that happened to them.

vulva. A girl's outside private part. This is all of the skin and body parts that protect the opening to the vagina.

Wrong Sexual Touching. When you touch a person in a mean or hurtful way, when you touch somebody else in their private parts without permission, or when somebody else touches you in your private parts without your permission. Also called **Wrong Touching.**

Wrong Thinking. When you make a mistake in your head. Wrong Thinking means a person is using Thinking Errors.

Wrong Touching. When you touch a person in a mean or hurtful way, when you touch somebody else in their private parts without permission, or when somebody else touches you in your private parts without your permission. Also called **Wrong Sexual Touching.**

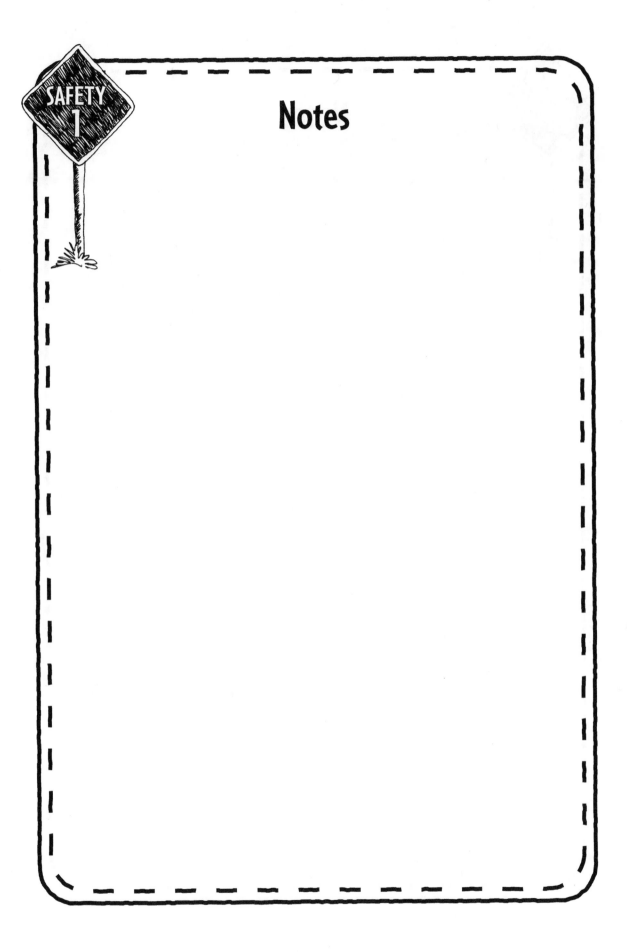

Notes

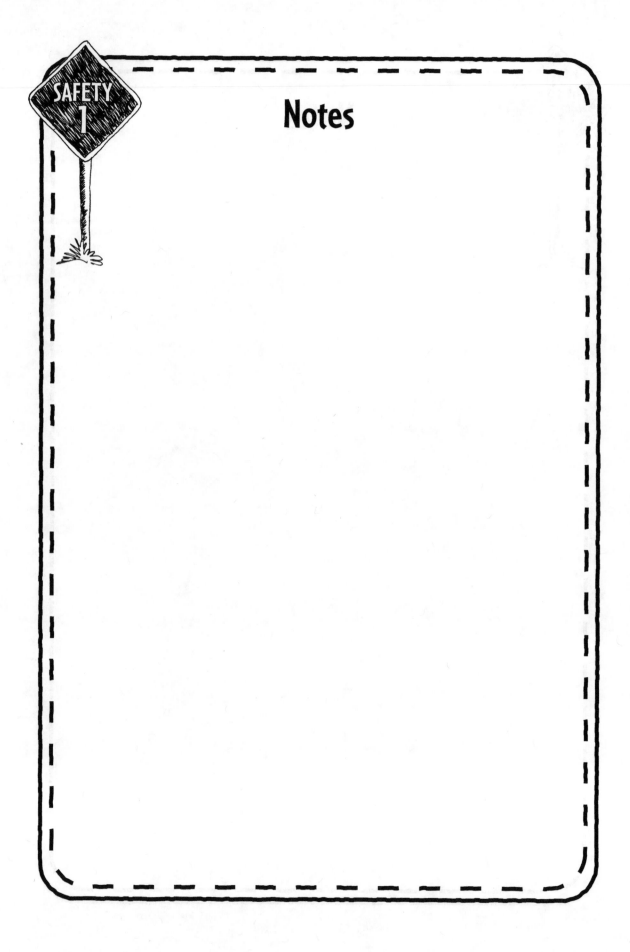

Notes

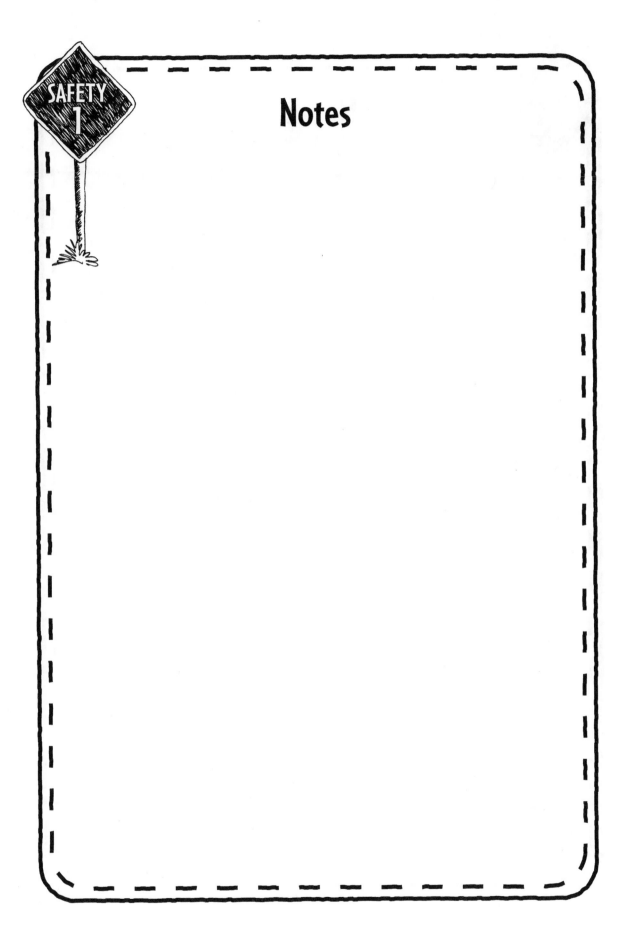

Notes

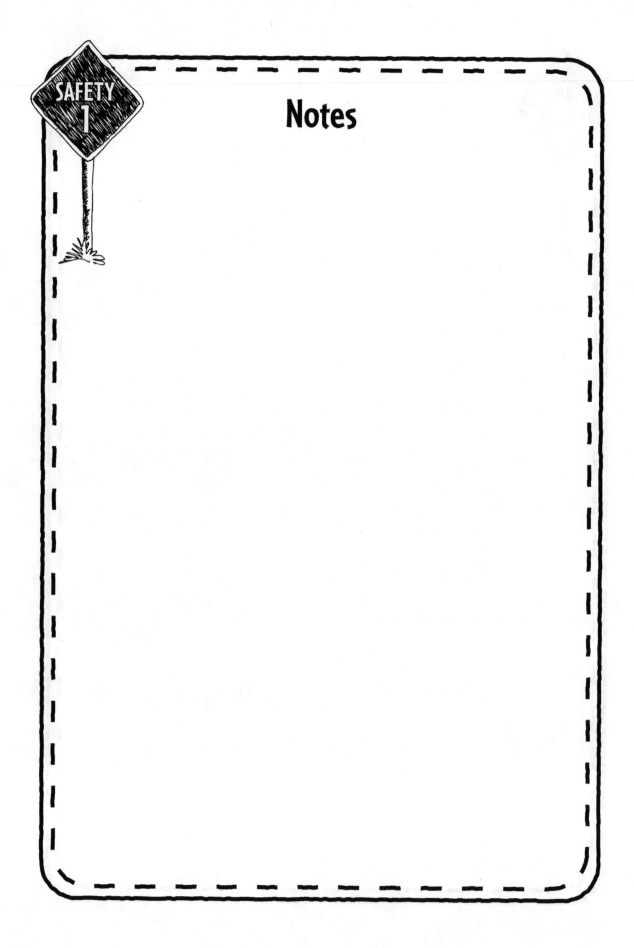

Notes

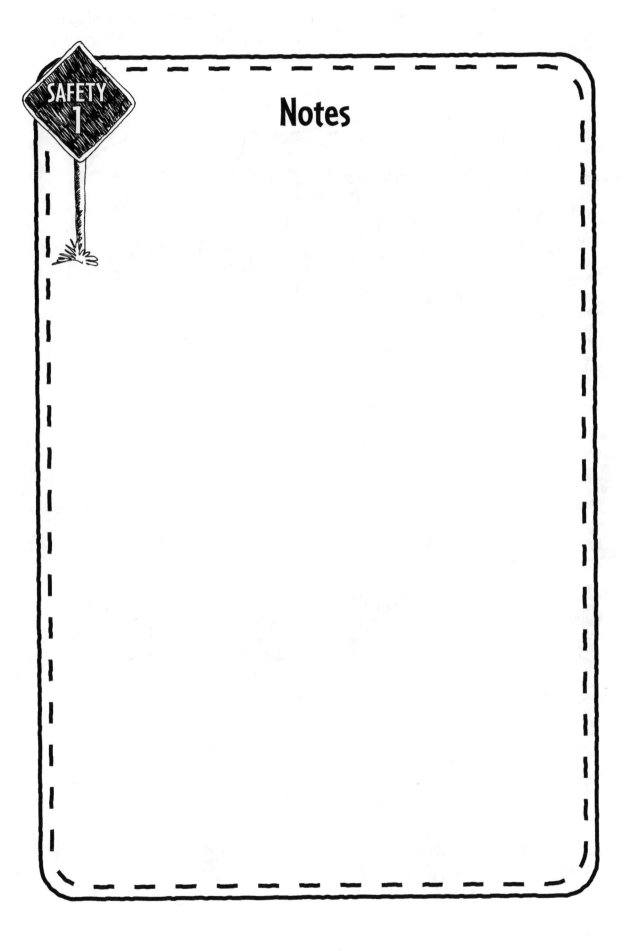

Notes

Color in this map to show how far you've come in your Roadmaps journey. You can color and decorate the road you've traveled, sights along the way so far, and the chapter you've just completed. You can use crayons, markers, colored pencils, or stickers.

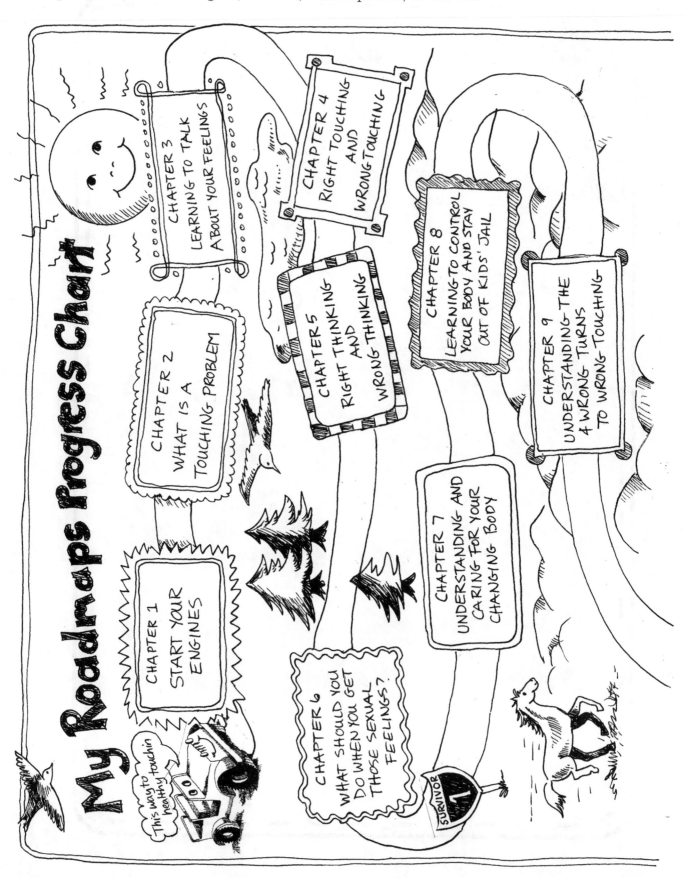

About the Author

Timothy J. Kahn is a nationally recognized clinician and trainer in the field of sexual offender and sexual behavior problem treatment. His well-known workbooks, *Pathways* and *Roadmaps* serve as models for the treatment process in programs across the country. He and his son Krishan Hansen, MSW, have coauthored *Footprints* (2005), a guided workbook for developmentally delayed adolescents and adults. Mr. Kahn is a clinical assistant professor with the University of Washington School of Social Work. From 1990 to 1998 he served as a member and as the chairman of the Washington State Department of Health Sex Offender Treatment Provider Advisory Committee, which developed evaluation and treatment standards and licensing requirements for sex offender treatment providers in Washington State. He has been instrumental in the development of training and treatment programs in Washington and British Columbia, and he regularly consults with a number of residential treatment programs and foster care agencies in the Pacific Northwest. He has served as an expert witness in numerous cases involving children with sexual behavior problems, sexual offenders, sexual misconduct, and sexual offender treatment. Tim currently maintains a private clinical and consultation practice in Bellevue, Washington, where he evaluates and treats children, adolescents, and adults with sexual behavior problems. He is a Certified Sex Offender Treatment Provider (WA. License #FC00000001), a Licensed Clinical Independent Social Worker, and a Licensed Mental Health Counselor. He is also a clinical member of ATSA, the Association for the Treatment of Sexual Abusers.